MINING IN SHROPSHIRE

Edited by Adrian Pearce
Shropshire Caving & Mining Club

Shropshire
Books

Front Cover: Granville Colliery
Back Cover Inset: Barytes miners at Wotherton, Chirbury

ISBN: 0-903802-63-5
Text: © Shropshire Caving and Mining Club 1995
Cover and Book Design by Paul Brasenell
Line Drawings by Malcolm Newton
Managing Editor: Helen Sample
Published by Shropshire Books the publishing imprint
of Shropshire County Council's
Information & Community Services Department
Printed in Great Britain by Livesey Limited

ACKNOWLEDGEMENTS

This book is the result of the combined efforts of the members of the Shropshire Caving & Mining Club. Apart from the chapter authors, we must thank numerous other members who helped with the exploration, surveying and research over many years and have made it all possible.

Many people in various roles have helped the Club to write this book.
Thanks are offered to all but especially to :-

Peter Eggleston	For organising the photos and illustrations.
Ken Lock	For information and photographs.
Tony Mugridge	For information on the Broseley area.
Malcolm Newton	For illustrations.
Donna Tomlins	For typing.
The Shropshire Records & Research Department	For permission to reproduce material.

A big debt of gratitude is also owed to all the landowners who have allowed us to explore their mines in the past. Please respect their property and, if you wish to visit the mines mentioned in this book, please use public rights of way or ask the landowners' permission.

The publishers would like to thank the following for permission to reproduce the illustrations in this book:

Malcolm Newton for his drawings	pp 3, 13, 31, 49, 70, 71, 72, 73, 75, 77, 80, 81, 83, 84, 85, 87, 88, 89, 90.
Shropshire Records and Research Unit	pp 10, 11, 37, 38, 60, 61, 62, 63, 89.
W Evans	pp 14, 15.
K C Lock	pp 16, 76, 78, 79, 82, 83, 88.
David Adams	pp 45, 46, 47, 49.
Steve Powell	pp 57, 58, 59, 66.
David Poyner	p 60.

MINING IN SHROPSHIRE

Richard K Morriss   p   67.
Clwyd-Powys Archaeological Trust   p   64.
All other photographs are owned by the Shropshire
Caving & Mining Club or I.A. Recordings.

ABOUT THE AUTHORS

THE SHROPSHIRE CAVING & MINING CLUB

We were formed in 1959 by a group of people interested in the exploration and study of disused mines in Shropshire and Wales. Since that time, the Club has expanded its interest to include caves and mines throughout Britain and Ireland. The activities of our members vary but the main ones are :-

- Exploration
- Surveying
- History & Publication
- Photography & Video Recording
- Geology
- Preservation

The Club produces a quarterly newsletter and an annual journal, as well as occasional publications called "Accounts" on specific mines or topics. We have also produced several videos on Shropshire mines. There is a large Club library providing a variety of publications, documents, plans, and information about caving and mining.

If you wish to become a Full Member, you first join as a Probationary Member until you have attended at least three trips with the Club. This allows us (and you!) to decide whether you have the right attitude to become a member. Underground exploration is potentially dangerous if you do not have the right equipment or skills and this is why we insist on this initial assessment period. Don't worry if you have never been underground before as we will train you in the necessary skills and lend you equipment for your first few trips. Those under sixteen join as Junior Members and can only attend Club trips where a Full Member takes responsibility for them. If you do not intend to join in the underground trips, you can become an Associate Member to receive the Newsletter and join in surface trips and social events.

The Club meets at 8pm on the first Friday of every month in the back room of the Last Inn at Church Aston near Newport. We discuss Club business, organise future

MINING IN SHROPSHIRE

trips, and have talks and slide shows. You are welcome to come along and talk to members. If you cannot attend these meetings but would like more information about our acitivities please write to the Secretary:

Adrian Pearce
72,Hopkins Heath,
Shawbirch, Telford,
Shropshire TF5 0LZ
Telephone: 01952 405369

His job done, the Editor returns to the depths!

CONTENTS

INTRODUCTION
Adrian Pearce

A mine that confirms people's expectations,
Blist's Hill Red Clay Mine.

To many people, mining means coal. This in turn conjures up visions of tall headgears,
chimneys belching smoke and huge spoil tips. Close by would be delapidated back to
back houses, smog and grime. Like watching an old black and white film - everything
would appear in shades of grey, even the miners trudging back home from the pit.
It was this bad public image that often led to the wholesale landscaping of mine sites
when they closed, leaving no visible trace of an industry that created and shaped
whole communities.

MINING IN SHROPSHIRE

Many villages and towns in Shropshire grew up around new mines and became wealthy as the mines prospered. It was not only the miners who depended on the mine for their livelihood, but also the local shopkeepers and farmers, blacksmiths, carpenters, builders and especially innkeepers. For the larger mines there were shareholders relying on dividends, often retired people hoping for a bonanza to supplement their income. The landowners received rent and royalties and many families made their wealth from mines. Some of these were absentee landowners such as the Marquis of Bath, Duke of Sutherland and Earl of Tankerville. All drew an income from the mines and it was a catastrophe for a community when a mine closed. In some places, the miners and their families moved elsewhere to find work and left ghost towns behind which rapidly became piles of stones.

Although coal was an important mineral, Shropshire was fortunate to have numerous other minerals which have been exploited in the past all over the county. Metals such as lead, copper, iron and zinc plus other materials such as clay, limestone and barytes were mined in the county and helped to shape the landscape and provide wealth. The industrial revolution could not have taken place without the mines that provided cheap raw materials.

Today we have no working mines left in Shropshire. They went even before the latest programme of pit closures. Except to the trained eye, most of the mine sites are now no more than humps and bumps in the landscape. There are some sites with visible remains but many are in danger of being forgotten. This book attempts to give a brief history and description of the various mining areas of Shropshire and describe what remains can still be seen. In some areas these are pitifully few but examples are listed in the field guides at the end of each chapter.

It must be stressed that many of the mine sites are on private land and, where this is the case, you should always ask permission before visiting them. The inclusion of a site in this book is no guarantee that there is a right of access. Remember that mine sites can still be dangerous, especially where there are ruined buildings or open entrances. You should never climb on old buildings or machinery. You should never explore mine workings unless you are properly equipped and experienced.

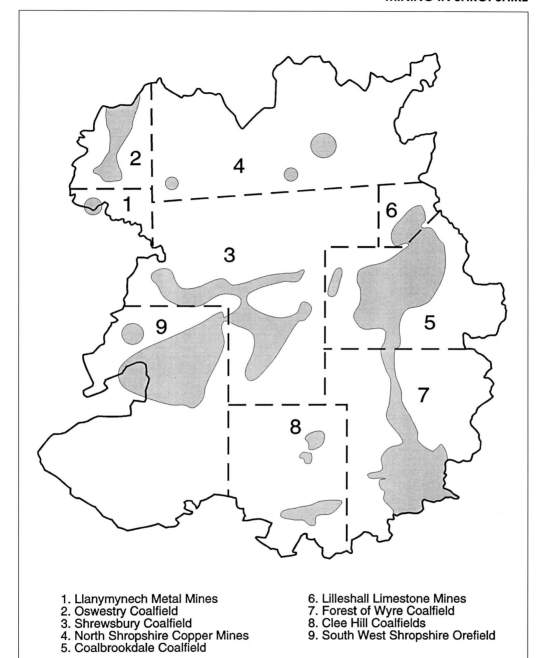

1. Llanymynech Metal Mines
2. Oswestry Coalfield
3. Shrewsbury Coalfield
4. North Shropshire Copper Mines
5. Coalbrookdale Coalfield
6. Lilleshall Limestone Mines
7. Forest of Wyre Coalfield
8. Clee Hill Coalfields
9. South West Shropshire Orefield

The Mining Areas of Shropshire

MINERALS

A great many minerals are found in Shropshire and few counties in Britain can say that they have mined a greater variety. The following section lists the minerals that have been mined in Shropshire:

Barytes or barium sulphate. Although the pure form is white, impurities cause it to be found in many colours. Used as drilling mud for the North Sea oil industry, an additive to paper and for medical and chemical purposes. The modern term is now barite.

Calcite or calcium carbonate. Its colouration is the same as barytes. Used as abrasive in toothpaste, pebbledash and decorative chippings.

Clay found in various consistencies and colours. Used to make pottery, pipes and tiles.

Coal found in varying qualities. Used mainly as a fuel.

Copper found as a carbonate (malachite), sulphate (azurite) or associated with iron (pyrites). All are smelted to obtain the metal.

Fluorspar or calcium fluoride. Found in the same colours as barytes. Used as a flux in smelting iron.

Fullers Earth a clay based material. It was used for de-greasing wool (fulling) and is now used by the military to combat chemical and nerve agents.

Iron found as various oxides. All are smelted to obtain the metal.

MINING IN SHROPSHIRE

Lead	mainly found as a sulphide (galena). Formerly used for roofing and plumbing but now used for battery plates and radiation proofing.
Limestone	occurs in several colours. Formerly used as building stone and in iron smelting.
Sandstone	occurs in several colours. Used as a building stone.
Silver	occurs with galena. It was tested and floated in a small dish or 'cupel' to obtain the metal.
Tar	occurred as pools which oozed from the rock. Was used to waterproof boots.
Vanadium	occurred in some places with copper deposits. It was used to make special steel.
Zinc	found as a sulphide (blackjack). Was smelted to obtain the metal.

LLANYMYNECH METAL MINES
Adrian Pearce

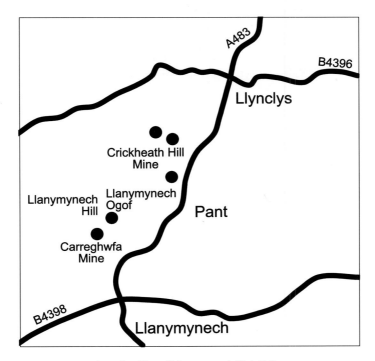

Location Map of Llanymynech Metal Mines

Llanymynech Hill lies five miles south-west of Oswestry and the summit is just over the Welsh border in Powys. The most obvious feature today is the disused quarry face but the area was once extensively mined for copper, lead and zinc.
Most of the hill is now part of a golf course but some mine entrances and spoil heaps have escaped being 'landscaped'. One of the entrances is called 'The Ogof' [Welsh for cave] and this could be one of the earliest sites of mining in the county.

The cave-like entrance chamber of Llanymynech Ogof in a gully next to the golf course.
The tiny entrance above it to the left is possibly pre-Roman.

There were two forts on the hill dating from the Bronze Age and excavations have revealed that copper smelting took place here. Copper is one of the main components of bronze and it would have been visible on the hill as a green stain in the rock. It thus seems very likely that copper was mined here, initially in surface pits and later in small underground passages.

It has already been proved elsewhere in Britain that copper was mined as far back as the Bronze Age, using primitive antler and bone picks to prize open cracks in the rock made by firesetting. This technique involved lighting a fire against the rock, causing it to expand with the heat. When water was thrown against it, the rock suddenly contracted and split. Copper was originally dug out of deep trenches but when the deposit became too deep, it had to be followed underground. Examples of small hand-picked passages have been found in and near to the Ogof and part of a deer antler was found in one, possibly a broken pick.

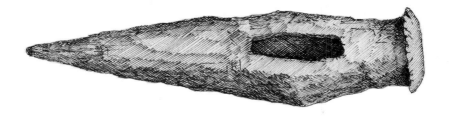

Two iron pick heads found in a Llanymynech mine in the 1750's, thought to be Roman

When the Romans arrived in the area, they found an existing copper mining industry and quickly exploited the Ogof for their own use. They had engineers with experience in other Roman mines and this allowed them to develop the workings in a more logical pattern. Mining was basically the same with firesetting and picking, although they used iron picks and wooden shovels with iron tips. Copper ore was placed in small wicker baskets and dragged out along the low passages. Slaves were used as miners and labourers. They were kept imprisoned in the mine and would rarely see the light of day. The lack of basic hygiene and ventilation probably meant that the slaves lead short and brutish lives. Over the years, a great many Roman artefacts have been found in the mine including a hoard of silver coins found by some schoolboys. Another strange feature has been the discovery of burials in and around the mine and bones may still be found amongst the rubble on the floor.

After the Romans left, the next period of activity was in the twelfth century. Most people have heard how King Richard I went to the Crusades and was captured on his return in 1193. Hubert Walter, the Bishop of Salisbury, had accompanied Richard and returned to England as one of the commissioners to raise money for his ransom. In his efforts to raise the required £100,000, he examined all possibilities and heard of the discovery of silver at the Carreghwfa Mine on Llanymynech Hill [lead ore containing silver occurs in the vicinity of the Ogof]. The Bishop decided to develop the mine and re-open the mint at Shrewsbury to refine the silver and make it into coins. To protect the mine, the nearby castle at Carreghwfa was repaired and provided with a garrison of troops. Despite the work that was carried out between 1194-95, very little silver was refined from the mine and the whole venture made a net loss.

There are many narrow winding passages in the Llanymynech mines,
such as this one near "The Belfry", which opens into a large chamber.

Later mining took place on the hill for lead and zinc but this must be one of the earliest mine sites in Shropshire and, with the ransom connection, perhaps the most fascinating. The hill again became notorious in the 1850s when a mining company duped its shareholders. This was a common occurrence in the nineteenth century but it is amazing how shareholders never seemed to learn their lesson. In short, a mining engineer would be paid to write a glowing report on the mine and the public encouraged to buy shares. The minimum capital possible would be spent on the mine and the rest went in fees and expenses to the directors. They could get away with it for a few years by saying that the mine needed to be developed before producing a profit. When the bubble burst, the directors would disappear.

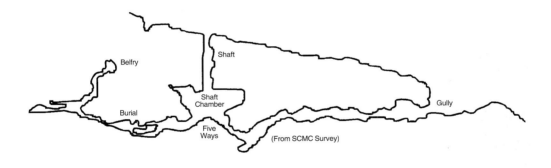

A cross-section through the workings of Llanymynech Ogof.

We cannot leave Llanymynech Hill without telling the story of Ned Pugh. In the nineteenth century, Ned is rumoured to have boasted that he could walk underground from the Ogof to the Lion Inn at Llanymynech. His friends did not believe him so he made a wager that the following Sunday he would play a tune underground beneath the Church. He would time his music to coincide with when the choir sang alone so that he could be heard by all the congregation. On the following Sunday, sure enough Ned took his harp and disappeared into the Ogof. To everyone's surprise, at the appointed time the congregation indeed heard the sound of a harp coming from below the ground. The singers took up the tune and when they finished the harp had ceased playing. Ned, however, never returned out of the Ogof and the tune was consequently called 'Farewell Ned Pugh'.

Descending a short winze or shaft during the 1960's exploration of Llanymynech Ogof.

One mile to the north-east is Crickheath Hill, where lead and zinc has been mined at several locations. It is not known if mining began at the same time as Llanymynech Ogof but it carried on until 1886, albeit on a small scale. There are several adits and shafts but all were worked under the name of Crickheath Hill Mine in the nineteenth century.

Field Guide

**Carreghwfa Mine
(SJ265218)**

All entrances have been filled in and only a few spoil mounds mark the ill-fated attempt to ransom King Richard.

Crickheath Hill Mine

There is very little to see on the surface as most remains have been obliterated by vegetation. Number 1 & 2 Levels (SJ275226) are open on either side of a small valley, Number 3 Level (SJ273231) and Number 4 Level (SJ272231) are open in a quarry to the left of a track and Number 5 & 6 Levels (SJ274232) are grilled in a quarry to the right of the track.

**Llanymynech Ogof
(SJ266222)**

A path passes between two spoil banks to a tall mine entrance which leads into the ancient workings. Just above and to the left of the entrance is a smaller entrance which may be pre-Roman. On the hillside above is a much later shaft into the workings and further to the right is an open nineteenth century adit.

OSWESTRY AND SHREWSBURY COALFIELDS

Stuart Tomlins

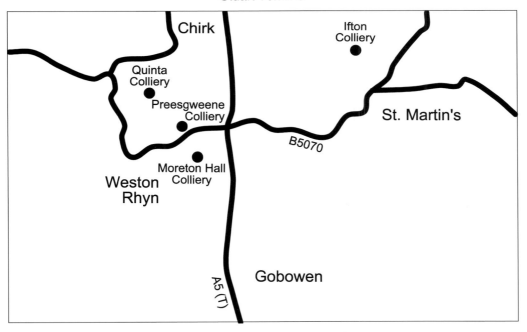

Location Map of Oswestry Coalfield

The Oswestry Coalfield was very active and is actually an extension of the Denbighshire Coalfield. The most famous pit was Ifton Colliery at St Martins, the largest colliery in Shropshire, which was connected underground to the old Brynkinallt and Black Park Collieries. Originally sunk as the Ifton Rhyn Colliery in the nineteenth century it eventually reached a depth of 1245ft. At its peak Ifton employed over 1,300 men. It closed in 1968 due to a loss of markets and underground fire problems. There were a number of other collieries to the west of St Martins, including Quinta, Preesgweene and Moreton Hall Collieries.

MINING IN SHROPSHIRE

Ifton Colliery Band

Ifton Colliery at the time of the pit closure in 1968

Miners at Ifton about to descend in a cage

Although the largest collieries were to the north of Oswestry, to the south-west lay the Morda valley with the oldest workings in the coalfield. One of the earliest references to this area is in the parish records dated 5th June 1595. This recorded the death of John Owen, *"smothered by a dump of the yearth in a colpit"*. Unfortunately, there are many other similar entries proving how dangerous an occupation it was.

Before the late eighteenth century, the workings would have been simple bellpits. After that time, technology was introduced with steam engines to wind and pump in the shaft. Some of the mine owners were particularly good to their men. In 1801, during a corn shortage, Sir Watkin of Trefarclawdd and Llwynymaen Collieries bought grain in bulk and sold it to the men at a reduced price. At the New British Colliery near Coed-y-Go there were few facilities so the owner Mr Savin opened a Tommy shop, butchers shop and tap room for his men. Tommy shops provided all sorts of groceries and hardware and some mine owners paid their men in tokens that could only be exchanged at their own Tommy shop. The owners of the Morda valley mines, however, do not seem to have done this and their men were paid in cash with no obligation to shop there.

One strange incident in 1831 became known as the 'Battle of Chirk Bridge'. Miners from the Wrexham area had been on strike to be paid in cash rather than tokens for Tommy

Preesgweene Colliery in 1873.

shops. They had heard that Oswestry miners were paid less than them and feared that their own wages would be reduced to that level. As a result, a crowd of them set out for Oswestry but were met by a party of Yeomanry at the border by Chirk Bridge. The miners were unarmed but a nasty incident was avoided when a small party of them were escorted into the town. They confirmed that the local miners were paid in cash with no obligation to shop at the mine owners' stores and returned home satisfied.

A number of collieries were worked in the nineteenth century but the last one, New Trefonen Colliery, closed in 1891. This ended the area's coal industry and many colliers moved to North Wales or Staffordshire.

The Shrewsbury Coalfield is situated to the south and south-west of Shrewsbury itself and is small by national standards. As it was conveniently situated to serve the domestic market of Shrewsbury, it is likely that mining was carried out here for many centuries. It also supplied fuel for smelting in the eighteenth and nineteenth centuries to the nearby lead mining area to the south. By the nineteenth century, there were nine reasonably sized collieries and many smaller ones. By 1921, these had all closed except for Hanwood Colliery which continued for a few years more until its closure in 1941.

One of the earliest references to coal mining in the Shrewsbury area was in 1727 in the will of Ann Gibbons of St Martins, who left all her Asterley coal pits, lands, gins, engines, tools and implements to her two sons Charles and Francis. Asterley appears to have been worked for coal for a considerable time and there were various pits in the area, mostly lying on the eastern side of Asterley village. Present day remains, however,

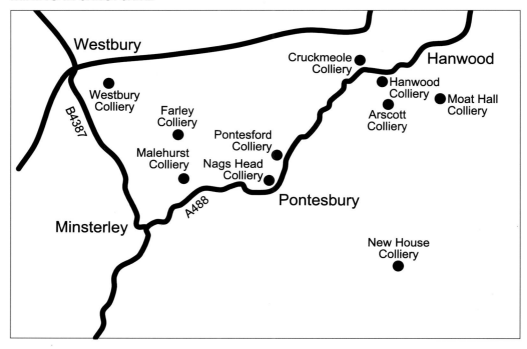

Location Map of Shrewsbury Coalfield

consist only of spoil tips since all shafts have been infilled over the years. The depths of the workings must vary, some are very shallow and there are reports of local farmers breaking into workings whilst digging land drains. About one mile north of Asterley there are more coal workings in Westbury Wood. Again, these appear to be very old with no remains apart from small tips and numerous depressions that may be subsidence caused by poorly-filled shafts or collapsed underground tunnels.

One mile south-east of Asterley is Malehurst Colliery which may be the site where, in 1775, a 'fire engine' was erected. If so, this is the first recorded steam pumping engine in this area. In 1778, Scott & Jeffries took out a fifty year lease on land belonging to the Boycott Estate north of Pontesbury which included the Malehurst Colliery and other mines. They purchased a 27" pumping engine from Boulton & Watt but the exact location of this engine is not known. Local place names give some clues to possible sites. Names such as 'Old Engine' and 'Big Engine' appear on large scale OS maps. An engine is also shown here on Baugh's map of 1808. Coal from Malehurst Colliery was sent to Pontesbury to be used in John Lawrence's smelt house and, when the colliery closed in 1795, Lawrence ensured continuing supplies by opening his own collieries nearby.

The nearby Pontesford Colliery was acquired by Probert, Lloyd, Jones & Co and in 1793 they installed a 33" engine for pumping. The enginehouse appears to have been built of wood and, although this would have been cheaper than stone, it would have increased

One of the two beam pumping enginehouses
of Pontesford Colliery which have been converted
into dwellings. The wooden wall through which
the beam once projected was long ago replaced
by the brick wall with the arched window.

The beam pumping enginehouse of Nags Head
Colliery (named after the local pub) only survives
as a picturesque brick and stone ruin.
In the far wall are holes for the timbers which
supported the beam floor.

the fire risk considerably. The engine is recorded as consuming 2,715 tons of coal in the period July 1808 to July 1811. This is an average of 2 tons per day but at least the colliery could produce the coal on site at no additional cost. From details of the pumps, it appears that the shaft was 225ft deep at that time. In 1831, John Lawrence ordered a new engine for the colliery and this was carried from Shrewsbury by a team of horses belonging to the Snailbeach Lead Mine Company. In the same year Messrs How, agents for Lord Tankerville, refused to allow the mine manager to break his contract and leave until the new engine had been installed. Another stone enginehouse was built about 1847, supervised by the engineer from Snailbeach Lead Mine. It is not known, however, whether this was to contain the original 33" engine or another purchased at a later date.

By the mid-nineteenth century, the rich Snailbeach Lead Mine Company had taken a major interest in the colliery, presumably to ensure coal supplies for their engine houses and smelting activities. A second-hand engine with a 20" diameter cylinder was purchased in 1859 for pumping and winding and the shaft at this time was 360ft deep. In 1862, the Snailbeach Mine daywork book records that the mine mechanic, Vincent Hughes, went to the colliery to take down the engine. This job took twelve days and it was taken to Snailbeach Mine where it was re-conditioned. This probably meant that the colliery had closed since the workings would flood rapidly without the engine. After Pontesford Colliery had closed, Snailbeach Lead Mine probably acquired its coal from the neighbouring Nags Head Colliery.

A few miles north-west was Westbury Colliery and this appears to have been a good sized undertaking for this area. In 1859, a lease was obtained by Thomas Davis and

MINING IN SHROPSHIRE

John Thomas from Edward Smythe-Owen of Condover Hall. This was for all pieces of land, enginehouses, buildings and erections totalling 13 acres and some other cottages, coal mines and 598 acres of land. The lease was to run for fourteen years at an annual rent of £50 for the land and cottages, plus royalties on the coal. The fact that there were existing enginehouses on the site indicates that the colliery had been in existence for some time before.

The partnership hit problems and John Thomas went bankrupt in September 1862. Following a visit by HM Inspector of Mines in October 1862, three summons were issued to Thomas Davis. The first was for failing to produce a plan of the workings, the second for not having an adequate brake attached to the steam engine used for winding men in the shaft and the third for not having a proper depth indicator on the steam winding engine. Smythe-Owen seems to have been concerned at the efficiency of the mine (since this would affect his royalty) and in November 1862 he instructed his attorney to try to get his lands back. With all these problems, the partnership decided to cease business and arranged for a valuation of equipment in February 1863 which came to £366.14.6d. Included in the list were the following :-

£115. 0.0	Steam engine with 30 " diameter cylinders, air pumps and condenser, iron beam with 6ft stroke, 2 air pump buckets with turned rods, 12ft balloon boiler, 16ft flywheel with spear rod, winding apparatus with large double crank, strong frame and holding down pins
£ 50. 0.0	12HP beam steam engine with winding apparatus gearing and boiler
£ 5. 5.0	166 yards of best two link chain
£ 2.10.0	60 yards of red deal pumping rods
£ 19. 0.0	30 yards of 14" pumps with clack door piece and working barrel
£ 3.10.0	Gin and strong frame
£ 2. 0.0	Pit frame with two large pulleys and roller posts

Close-up of rope marks on bridge.

Cruckmeole Colliery which became part of the Hanwood and Moat Hall Company.
The bridge parapet in the centre background still shows rope marks from the cable-hauled tramway incline.

To the north of Westbury, there are old workings dating from the 1850's in the area around Coedway and Crewgreen. Scattered remains can be seen here but they are only spoil mounds and collapsed shafts. There are no remains of masonry structures and it seems likely that these were small concerns with only wooden surface buildings. A few years ago a brick-lined shaft opened up in a farmer's field near Halfway House, close to the A458. It was filled and made safe by British Coal.

Further east, Arscott Colliery operated by a Mr Smallshaw appears to have closed around 1920 when the lease expired, the men transferring to Hanwood Colliery. The closure caused a great deal of concern to the neighbouring Cruckmeole Colliery which experienced increased water inflow after pumping stopped at Arscott. Hanwood Colliery was started in the 1870s and, although originally a small independent venture, it eventually became the biggest in the coalfield. In 1921, the Hanwood & Moat Hall Collieries (Salop) Ltd was formed and managed by Nicholas Fielden. The company acquired the old Hanwood, Moat Hall, Cruckmeole and Arscott Collieries and combined them together to work under the name of Hanwood Colliery. At its peak, the colliery employed about 300 men drawn from Hanwood, Westbury, Pontesbury, Hookagate and Annscroft. It was a major employer and its closure in 1941 was a serious blow to the communities.

*Perry Mansell (left) and
Walter Challinor at the face of
Hanwood Colliery in the 1920s.
The undercut seam is about to be
broken down to win the coal, all by
the light of the candle stuck to the
rocks with a lump of clay.*

During the nineteenth century, eight shafts had been sunk on the Moat Hall and Hanwood sections and these varied in depth from 75-450ft. The deepest workings were in the 'Half-Yard Seam' which provided a quick lighting and free burning coal. This was much in demand locally and in Central Wales as far out as the coast. Hanwood coal was very widely known in this area and it was even sent down to South Wales at one point. One advantage of Hanwood was that the coal was free from gas and this allowed the use of naked flames underground.

*A pit pony about to go underground
at Hanwood Colliery in the 1930s.
From left Walter Challinor,
Edwin Thomas (horse driver),
George Cooper, Charles Cooper
and Mr Bolton.*

One of the first innovations of the new company was to erect an electricity generating station on the surface at Cruckmeole. This allowed the introduction of electric pumps, fans, lighting and underground haulage. The latter was very important as the workings were on a steep slope. Even so, three pit ponies were kept underground for haulage duties and were perhaps unique in that they were brought back up in the cage each night instead of being stabled at the pit bottom. Electricity was also used to operate the screens at Cruckmeole. These sorted the coal into four grades which were large coal, nuts, steam peas and dust. The latter was not commercially viable but was used as a cheap fuel for the company's own boilers at Cruckmeole.

Field Guide

**Ifton Colliery
(SJ322373)**

The site is now used by other firms but a number of old colliery buildings still remain, including the pithead baths and office block. A small coal tub mounted on rails has been preserved as a memorial to the mine and the miners welfare building still survives in the village. If you feel active, the line of the mineral railway can be followed to its junction with the main line at Preesgweene.

**Nags Head Colliery
(SJ408064)**

This is situated opposite the Rea Valley Tractors garage on the outskirts of Pontesbury. In a clump of trees to the south of some cottages is a spoil tip and the ivy-covered remains of the enginehouse in a very poor state.
The engine pumped from a circular shaft immediately in front of the lever wall. A further enginehouse on the south side of the river has been incorporated into two cottages. It is a small building with three storeys but there is little to see of interest due to extensive alterations.

**Pontesford Colliery
(SJ410067)**

An enginehouse stands to its full height and the facade has been changed very little since the engine was removed.
The lever wall opening has been blocked up and the building converted into a dwelling. The boiler house was incorporated into the local blacksmith shop which was built onto the west wall. Inside, there are three storeys and the pit is used as a cellar. The spoil tips around the building have been converted into a private car park and the shaft has been capped. In 1969, it was occupied by a Mrs Davies, whose family had lived there for three generations. Her father, who died in 1932 at the age of 89, was born there so the engine must have been removed before 1840.

NORTH SHROPSHIRE COPPER MINES

Geoff Warrington

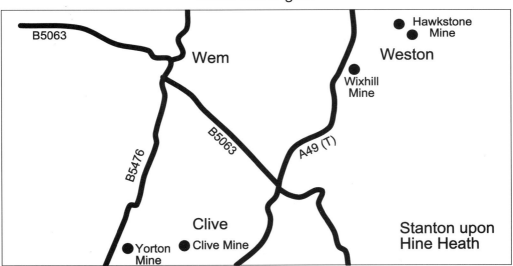

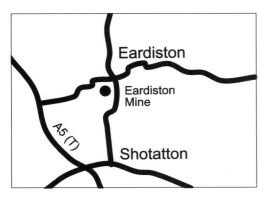

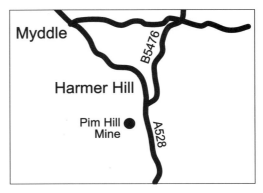

Location Maps of North Shropshire Copper Mines

MINING IN SHROPSHIRE

The land to the north of Shrewsbury is fairly flat but, where the isolated wooded hills occur, copper was often found in the Triassic sandstone as green malachite. It was mined at a number of places but most of the sites are now overgrown and difficult to recognise.

The most westerly site is Eardiston Mine and the earliest reference was in 1826 when 'Jones the lime man' sank three shafts. These were all 30ft deep but earlier mining had taken place and the copper had presumably been removed already. Jones seems to have given up in disgust and it was not until 1836 that a Liverpool partnership led by Robert Parry took over the mine. The lease was only for one year and it stipulated that a tenth of all copper ore raised (usually converted to the cash equivalent) was paid to the landowner. A minimum of four miners were to be kept at work during the whole period. If the mine proved worthwhile, there was an option to extend the lease for 21 years but increase the dues to one eighth of ore raised.

It seems that the partners did extend the lease and about 2,500 tons of ore were mined between 1841-45. There are conflicting reports but the workings seem to have been at a depth of between 100-180ft. Some £8,000 had been spent on equipping the mine but the returns did not repay the outlay. Before the introduction of railways, the ore was taken two miles by cart to a canal wharf at Queens Head, Rednal. From here it went to the copper smelters at St Helens and Liverpool. A visiting geologist in November 1842 recorded that water from a depth of 96ft had a temperature of over 50° Fahrenheit while that on the surface was frozen. Mining ceased again but the mine was re-opened briefly in 1862 to pay for the building of a chapel midway between Ruyton and West Felton. The work must have been done by locals and it was apparently finished within three years.

The entrance to an adit cut in a sandstone cliff which leads
to the filled shafts and workings of Eardiston Mine.

In 1864, the mine was acquired by the British Copper Co Ltd and by the following year they were producing up to 60 tons of 'high quality' ore per month. This was not enough to repay the costs, however, and the company went into liquidation during 1865.
The company brought in several respected mine captains (experienced managers) from other mines to report on the future prospects. They claimed to be favourably impressed but such people always were, when paid to help sell shares to potential investors! As nobody was gullible enough to believe them, the mine never worked again and the company was finally dissolved in 1882.

To the east of Eardiston lies Pim Hill. King Charles I witnessed mining here in 1643 when he visited the area. It ceased immediately when the miners joined the army being raised by the King. Their stock of copper ore, 'a sort of blue stone', was subsequently used in road works so we can assume that the miners did not return from the Civil War.
In the latter part of the seventeenth century, Derbyshire miners were employed to search for copper ore on behalf of the Earl of Bridgewater. They sank several trial shafts, one apparently reaching a depth of 180ft. Despite all this, they found little ore and mining ceased by the turn of the century.

Crawling out to the surface from the Pim Hill Mine. The entrance had been filled in until an SCMC member dug it out. There are pick marks in the sandstone walls and the smooth shape of pre-gunpowder mining.

The mine was leased for fourteen years in 1710 by the Countess of Bridgewater to Abraham Darby & Company, who had been involved in the brass industry in Bristol before moving to Coalbrookdale. Darby may have retained this interest and tried to obtain a local source of copper for brassmaking. The site did not live up to his expectations, however, and by 1714 he was importing copper from the Lake District.
The only other recorded period of working was between 1870-75 when copper, cobalt and vanadium were mined.

MINING IN SHROPSHIRE

Just to the north-east of Pim Hill near Yorton, was a shaft reputed to be 150ft deep which would also have been for copper but lack of firm evidence means it must remain a mystery.

Further east near the village of Clive are the remains of the largest known copper workings in Shropshire. There are several small handpicked shafts leading into shallow workings which suggest that part of the mine is very old, perhaps dating from the seventeenth century. The number of shafts and their spacing also suggest that these were separate small scale workings, perhaps mined on a part-time basis by farm workers who were laid off in winter. Records reveal a Drepewood or Threapwood Mine in the area which was worked in 1710 by Thomas Oswin, and a Spendiloes Mine near Grinshill Church which Roger Acherley proposed to develop in 1711.

The mine was probably worked on a small scale for many years until 1862 when the Clive Copper Mining Co Ltd was formed to acquire the site. Three years later the company was offering the lease for sale at £4,000 and the New Clive Mining Co Ltd bought in 1865. Most of the shareholders of the new company were from Birmingham and they spent a great deal of money but *"did no good"*. The workings are still accessible to experienced mine explorers. The upper level in the mine was enlarged to produce chambers up to 20ft wide and 30ft high which have cut off the bottom of the

Mine House at Clive. The small building stands over the well shaft. The narrow doorway may once have accommodated the belt drive from a portable steam engine to drive the pumps.

older workings and the old shafts can now be seen from below. The copper deposit in the upper level eventually ran out to the north and was not found again, despite desperate searching. The miners cut a lower level but there are few mineral traces at this depth. A shaft up to the surface was deepened to form a well when the mine closed.

Looking up the well shaft at Clive from a landing 50 metres below ground. To the left is the pump rising main with the old pump rods on the right.

A short hand-picked level leading to a filled shaft in Clive Copper Mine. It is cut through sandstone that shows beautiful whorls and lines of blue-green and brown 'Liesegang Rings' where the copper and iron mineralisation has formed natural patterns.

The copper leaching tanks from Clive Mine built of slabs of sandstone from the nearby Grinshill Quarry. The tanks are now at Bryntail Lead Mine in Powys.

MINING IN SHROPSHIRE

By 1869 the ore had run out and the company was selling off the mine's equipment, including a set of stone troughs for precipitating copper which are now preserved at the Bryntail Mine in Wales. As the copper ore was intermixed with sandstone, it had to be crushed and covered with hydrochloric acid in the stone troughs to dissolve out the copper. The liquid was transferred to other troughs containing scrap iron. The copper steadily precipitated onto the iron which was eventually removed so the copper sulphate could be scraped off. From the excavations in Clive Mine we can estimate that 20,000 tons of rock was removed producing 200 tons of copper metal.

A level wall in Clive Mine, showing well-preserved pick marks and also soot marks from candles that were placed in small notches cut in the wall. Notice the sooty graffiti on the roof.

Exploring the Grotto at Hawkstone Park. This is a folly cut in sandstone and once faced with shells and crystals. It was hollowed out right next to the shafts of an early copper mine.

To the north-east there was mining somewhere near Lee Brockhurst and mine shafts on the Terrace at Hawkstone Park but these were filled-in years ago. In 1697 local landowners formed a partnership to mine copper and other ores at these locations but it could only have been on a small scale. By 1740 the Reverend Snelson had searched for copper ore at Weston but *"had his labour for his pains, and his expence for his trouble"* (an epitaph that applies to many other mining ventures). Small scale mining also seems to have continued at Weston until the early nineteenth century and there was a brief period of re-working at Wixhill between 1865-67.

Field Guide

Clive Mine (SJ514239)   Mine House was one of the mine buildings and in front of it a small building covers the pumping shaft now converted to a well. The building once contained a steam engine to operate pumps in the shaft.

Eardiston Mine (SJ366246)   The enginehouse foundations remain but the shaft has been filled. An adit can be seen on the other side of the road.

The top of a shaft in Clive Mine.
The planks and lifeline allow modern
explorers to cross safely over the void.

One of the large excavations of Clive Mine. The wall on the left is one side of the fault and the smooth parts of the wall are 'slickensides' where rock has been polished by geological movement.

COALBROOKDALE COALFIELD

David Coxill & Kelvin Lake

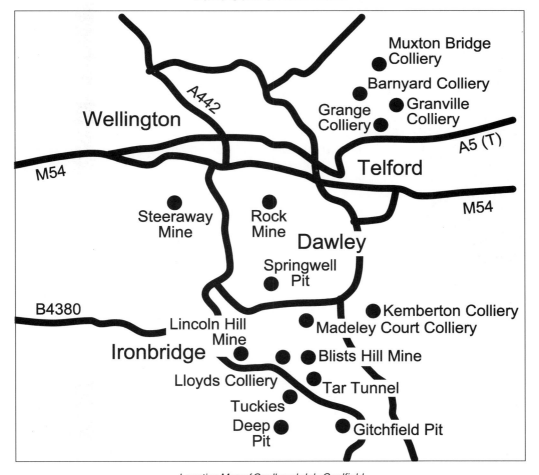

Location Map of Coalbrookdale Coalfield

MINING IN SHROPSHIRE

A casual visitor to the Ironbridge Gorge in the seventeeth century would have wondered what was in store for them as they descended the steep hill from Madeley to the River Severn. A scene full of smoke and fumes belching forth from numerous blast furnaces, lead smelters, tar distilleries, brick and tile works would have lain before them. Squeezed between these works were dozens of mines tipping their waste onto the river banks, while a seemingly endless stream of trucks and carts carried coal and other minerals to the gaping mouths of furnaces and kilns. Apart from the sites preserved as industrial monuments and museums, little now remains of all this activity.

The steep sides of the Gorge were a natural place for exploiting numerous exposed seams of coal, ironstone, clay, fullers earth, sandstone and limestone. In addition, the densely wooded hillside would have provided a good supply of timber for charcoal. Exactly when mining started in the area is not known but the Romans used coal in their underfloor heating at nearby Wroxeter. There is evidence that they worked small coal mines near Oakengates. It seems reasonable to suppose that the Romans could also have made some attempt at mining in the Gorge.

By the Middle Ages, mining was well established in the area. The first reference was in 1250 when Philip de Benthall granted the Buildwas monks a right of way over his land to carry coal and ironstone. Since mining began to deplete the local forests of timber, a proclamation was made in 1308 banning the use of coal as a fuel. This does not appear to have been strictly obeyed as fourteen years later Wenlock Priory granted a licence *"for the digging of coles at the Brocholes (Madeley)"*. The monastic settlements of Wombridge Priory, Buildwas Abbey and Much Wenlock were amongst early exploiters of the local mineral resources. The Buildwas monks operated a system whereby people who worked for them could cover their debts to the Abbey, such as rent, by working at certain times of the day without pay. Occasionally during periods when mines could not be worked, the miners were given a quantity of ale in lieu of pay. This system, known as 'Buildwases', carried on until the mid-nineteenth century.

There was widespread mining of ironstone by the sixteenth century to feed the growing number of furnaces in the area. In 1535, Wombridge Priory earned five pounds per year from one of their mines and in 1541 Wenlock Priory had an iron mine valued at £2 6s 1d. James Clifford, Lord of the Manor of Broseley and owner of the Boat Leasow Mine, was ordered in 1575 to remove rubbish and stone that he had thrown into the deepest part of the River Severn from his *"coaldelf at a place called the Tuckeyes"*. This mine is known to have worked for almost three hundred years but was capped and built over by Maw's & Co when they constructed their works at Jackfield.

By the seventeenth century, the Coalbrookdale Coalfield was the second most important coal mining district in the country. It produced 95% of all the coal mined in Shropshire and was only surpassed in output by the North East Coalfield. Despite this, it only covered about 24 square miles in area from the Severn to Shifnal and Wellington to Bridgnorth. At this time, coal was mostly used for the brick and tile industries and for export, and the most important mineral was ironstone for use in charcoal fired blast furnaces.

Abraham Darby's success in smelting iron using coked coal in 1709 changed all that. As industrialisation of the Gorge began after 1709, there came an unprecedented demand for coal, iron and limestone. Limestone came from mines at Steeraway, The Hatch, Little Wenlock, Lilleshall and Church Aston, coal and iron were mined all along the Gorge and clay was mined south of the River Severn. During this period, large companies were formed and the coalfield was eventually divided up between the Madeley Wood Company in the south and the Lilleshall Company in the north.

The early mines were opened as adits or drift mines, tunnels driven into the side of a valley following a workable seam. A local name for these was 'footrids', although some Broseley people call a clay level a *"Stocking of Clay"*. Until recent years, the entrances to several footrids were open near the picnic site on the Broseley side of the Iron Bridge. One of these was unusual in that the entrance was supported by steel girders. These were all demolished in the 1970s during landscaping operations and only shallow trench-like depressions remain near the path on the Benthall Edge Nature Trail.

Attempts by the Shropshire Caving & Mining Club to explore adits in the Gorge have often been thwarted by bad air. This can be methane (fire damp) in coal levels or carbon dioxide (black damp) in clay or ironstone levels. Hydrogen sulphide (stink damp) is often found where there are natural bitumen or tar deposits. The term 'damp' is an obsolete term for gas but it is still used in mining circles. Concentrations of these gases build up in the levels and it cannot be stressed too strongly that the casual visitor should not explore mines as old pockets of gas could prove fatal.

The late Alderman T Jones, a Broseley mining entrepreneur, used to recall how the Red Church Pennystone Pit, a local iron mine, was plagued with black damp.

The hand windlass over the escape shaft of Gitchfield Pit at Jackfield is a very rare survivor.
The lever operates a crude band brake.

MINING IN SHROPSHIRE

The miners claimed that it was *"damper"* when the wind was from the south and on one occasion the fireman inspected the mine on two consecutive days and declared it *"unsafe to work due to damp"*. On the third day the fireman looked at the church weather cock and decided that it was not worth inspecting the mine since the wind was shown as blowing from the south. What he did not know was that two miners had climbed the tower and wedged the weather cock in position, the pit was off work for a week before they were found out!

To overcome ventilation problems in long levels, shafts were often dug higher up the hill to help create a through draught. These could also be used as emergency escape routes if the main level collapsed. If the material had to be taken up the hill it could be wound up the shaft in a basket or 'kibble'. In shallow pits, the winding gear would be a simple hand-operated windlass called a 'jackroller' or 'jinny'. Sometimes the rope was not completely wound onto the drum but only had a few turns around it, a counterweight then balancing the weight of the kibble. The last windlass of this type was used until 1964 at Rock Mine but it has not survived. At the time of writing there is still a jackroller over the escape shaft of Gitchfield Pit at Jackfield.

Rope used on early windlasses was made of hemp but this tended to break when wet. To help preserve ropes, they were coated in local tar which was often found oozing from tunnel walls, such as can still be seen in the Tar Tunnel at Coalport. In later years,

This abandoned coil of winding rope shows the hemp core surrounded by strands of steel wire, typical of one era of winding technology.

locally invented chains were used and then wire ropes. The rope on the drum at Gitchfield is a wire rope with a hemp core, this makes it more flexible and allows it to be wound onto a smaller diameter drum.

Gitchfield Mine was typical of hundreds of footrids. It was driven in 1891 to provide clay for the Coalport Tileries. The area is now the Coalport sewage works and the adit entrance no longer exists, although water coming out of the level has been used as a water supply for the works. It closed in the 1950s and its method of operation was the same as many small mines in the area. Material cut at the face was pulled by children on wooden sleds (known as 'mobbies') to the main roadways, where it was transferred to wagons (known as 'dans') that were pulled out of the mine by horses. Girls were used for this job until the 1844 Mines Act, after which only boys were used. In 1892, the thirteen year old W Yates of Madeley started work at Gitchfield as a 'mobbier'. During a working day he would crawl on his hands and knees pulling two sleds at a time behind him. The haulage chain or rope from the sleds was attached to a metal D-ring on a thick leather belt, which was worn tightly around the waist to prevent chaffing. As the D was worn at the front, with the chain passing between the legs, the excessive loads they pulled meant that by their twenties mobbiers would often suffer from severe hip and leg displacement. An example of a 'mobbie' and harness can be seen at the Ironbridge Gorge Museum.

In deep pits where the loads were quite heavy, horse powered 'gins' (short for engine) were used. Two types were used locally. The 'gear pit' system was the simplest with the horse attached directly to the load and made to walk away from the shaft. This had its drawbacks for, if the horse lost its footing, it could be dragged back towards the shaft. The more complex 'gin pit' involved one or two horses being used to turn a large wooden drum, from which the rope ran to the shaft over rollers. Due to the abundance of wood and cheap operating costs, gins were quite a popular winding technique for shafts between 100-300ft deep. When a horse gin was erected at a new mine, it was the custom to hold a 'gin rearing' party with free ale, bread and cheese being supplied by the landowner. The last 'gin rearing' was held in 1910. Remains of gins could be found at Deep Pit, Broseley and Lightmoor near Madeley as recently as the 1940s and one was still working near Madeley until 1948.

Reconstruction of typical horse gin.

MINING IN SHROPSHIRE

Although old technology survived in the coalfield until relatively modern times, it would be wrong to think that the mine owners and industrialists in this area were slow to implement new ideas. One of the most important innovations of the area in the seventeenth century was the development of the longwall system of mine working. This replaced the earlier pillar and stall system where only about 30% of the seam was removed, the remainder being left to support the roof and reinforce the floor. The longwall system, or "Shropshire Method" as it became known, rapidly spread to other mining areas as it allowed almost all of a seam to be removed as workings advanced from or (as in modern pits) retreated towards the shaft bottom. The space left behind by mining is known as the 'gob' or 'goaf' and it is packed with waste rock and left to collapse.

An early photograph of a horse gin at Lightmoor near Telford.
The horse walked round the drum on the right and wound in the shaft behind the hut on the left.
The drum was counterwound so, as one bucket descended, another ascended.

The centre post of a horse gin had been used as a gate post until the SCMC rescued it in the mid-1960s.

In a private garden on the hillside above Ironbridge, is a 50 metre long brick-lined adit into an old iron mine. It worked the Crawstone ironstone using the longwall system over a hundred and fifty years ago, but in an unusual way. The miners started at the centre and then worked outwards, using sandstone packs to support the roof, creating an ever expanding circular longwall. This mine is now too dangerous to explore due to gas.

John Wilkinson the local ironfounder built the first coal cutting machine in 1780. The 'iron man' was introduced to the Broseley mines where it cut down the side of the coal after it had been undercut. The machine worked very well in the thicker seams but the miners saw it as a threat to their jobs. They refused to set roof supports for the machine, claiming that *"if the iron men can do one job they can also do the other"*. One tradition in the area was that of the 'chartermaster', who acted as a labour subcontractor to the owner. Many of these owned tommy shops from where miners under their employment were expected to buy their goods, often at inflated prices for poor quality. This tradition survived into the present century and the last chartermaster retired from Granville Mine in 1913.

A brick built beam enginehouse at Trench about to be demolished in 1964.
If it had survived just a few more years it would, of course, have been unthinkable
to destroy such an important industrial monument.

MINING IN SHROPSHIRE

The first atmospheric steam engine in Shropshire was erected at the Madeley Glebe coalworks in about 1719, only seven years after Newcomen's first engine was installed at Dudley. This and other early engines were used for pumping water, allowing deeper seams to be worked. Water was always a problem in the Coalbrookdale Coalfield and a miner who worked at Granville Colliery in the 1920s recalled working in a 3ft seam with 6-9" of water in it. The seam was so wet that it was like working in a permanent shower, sometimes if the 'rain' was very bad they would be allowed to leave an hour or so earlier. During the 1940s he was paid an extra 2/- per day for wet working.

Large firms with several adjacent mines would often erect central pumping engines to drain them all. The Lilleshall Company on the northern side of the coalfield drained Muxton Bridge, Waxhill Barracks and Barnyard Collieries through a shaft at Muxton which pumped 9,350 gallons per hour. In the Severn Gorge at least two central engines existed. The Madeley Wood Company had an engine pumping at The Lloyds and, on the other side of the river at the Tuckies, an engine was installed about 1780 to drain several mines including Boat Leasow Mine. The Tuckies enginehouse still survives although it was converted into a dwelling in the 1840s with an adjoining house added in the 1880s. During alterations in 1983, the joists of the first floor were found to have curved cut-outs in the middle where they had once supported the steam cylinder. The second floor joists were very thick and had obviously been the original beam floor, with the one end wall about 3ft thick that had supported the engine's beam. The 150ft deep pumping shaft was still open, although covered with a concrete slab and a garden shed!

The three storey building is the shell of the 1780 Tuckies pumping enginehouse, during conversion into a dwelling. The two small holes in the back wall supported the 'spring timbers' of the beam floor.

In the early years, it was customary to give injured miners the job of tending the steam pumping engines. As winding engines began to be introduced in the 1780s to wind material and men, the job of attending these was usually given to a more *"respected and sober"* person. Once someone was appointed to the job of winding engineman, it was usually passed down from father to son. Men were initially wound up and down the shaft in a kibble or by *"riding the chain"* - hanging onto loops fitted to the wrought iron winding chain. These chains were made locally and, after 1810, were typically made of three parallel lengths of chain keyed together with wooden pegs.

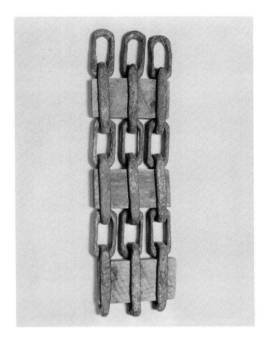

A short length of Shropshire winding chain or 'rattle chain'. The wooden blocks between the alternate links prevented the chains tangling and helped them lie flat across the winding spool.

Shropshire was noted for its use of winding chain despite the introduction of flat wire ropes in the 1840s. Local chain makers did not switch to wire rope making until after several local accidents, notably the tragic death of nine miners at the Brick Kiln Leasow Pit, Madeley in 1864. They were killed when the chains became unhooked as the men were ascending the shaft. A further eight miners were killed *"riding the chain"* at Springwell Pit, Dawley in 1872 because there was no cage and the chain was old and worn. Despite this, many local pits carried on using chain well into this century.

One of the last winding enginemen at Blists Hill Mine (now reconstructed by Ironbridge Gorge Museum) was Frank Turner. His typical routine in the mid 1930s was to arrive at work about 6.15am. The stoker Billy Lewis, from the All Nations pub, would have arrived at 6am to get the steam ready. The cage was first wound down empty so that the Banksman could check the main cable and then the Manager and Onsetter would be wound down, standing on top of the cage to check the guide wires and shaft. At the bottom, they would inspect the workings to check for gas and other problems.

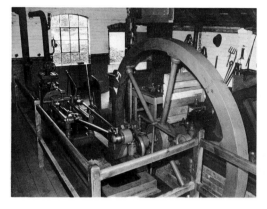

Old winding chain and rope (top) was often used as fencing. Here are three lengths of flat wire rope stapled to a Shropshire fence post.

The steam winding engine at Blists Hill (above) was rescued from Milburgh Tileries on the other side of the Severn.

The reconstructed winding engine in operation at the Ironbridge Gorge Museum.

While the pit was being inspected, Frank would cook his breakfast on a stove in the enginehouse and miners arriving for work would creep past so as not to disturb his 'snappin' and suffer a rough ride down! The inspection was usually finished by 6.50am and, after the safety book had been signed, the miners would be wound down in groups of six so they were at work by 7am. They worked through to 3pm, often in one foot of water since this was a very wet mine. When the Lloyds pumping engine was stopped in 1911, water was wound out of the pit in a large kibble (in a second shaft).
The kibble went down as the cage came up and then vice versa. The water was emptied into a trough draining into the canal and in hot weather local children came to paddle in the icy cold water. Frank would often work until 6pm (4.30pm on Saturday and Sunday) to get the water down to a safe level.

The Rock Fireclay Mine near Ketley was worked up to 1964. A large amount of underground equipment was salvaged by the SCMC for Ironbridge Museum.

Miners finishing their shift at Granville in January 1974.

Coal production reached a peak in Shropshire in 1871 when over one million tonnes were produced, iron production peaking two years later. By the beginning of the twentieth century, however, many of the mines were worked out and began to close. The last limestone mine at The Hatch closed in 1918, ironstone mining ceased in the 1940s and the last fireclay mine at The Rock closed in 1964. By nationalisation, only three deep collieries were still at work at Kemberton, Grange and Granville. Kemberton Colliery closed in 1967 as the coal became exhausted. The last small coal mine at Shortwoods closed in 1970. In 1979, Granville Colliery (which by then had merged with Grange) finally closed and with it came the end of deep coal mining in Shropshire. Today it is more economical to opencast and this is currently being done around Telford for coal and fireclay.

Granville miners voting to return to work in March 1974

(Above) Opencast pits often reveal ancient shaft and tunnel mines. Here at Symon opencast near Dawley an old roadway has been reconstructed with timber props, plate rails and flanged wheels.

(Left) Granville pit after closure in January 1990.

Mine tubs running on narrow gauge rails were once common in the area. Shropshire mines also used plate rails for much longer than elsewhere.

Old accounts of working life in the past can often seem charming and simple but in truth it was very grim. One old Granville miner started work at fourteen, removing tubs from the cage at the pit bottom. He only just had time to push one tub away, return and push the second tub away before the next cage load arrived. Where he worked, the roof bulged down and he once cut the full length of his back open on a girder. At the end of a shift he would go home still covered in dirt and fall asleep on the couch, without having any food or drink.

Although this coalfield did not have the big mining disasters that other areas did, thousands of lives have been lost from accidents, such as roof falls, fires, accumulations of gas, people falling down shafts or winding accidents. Lodgebank Colliery was renamed 'Slaughter Pit' after 1875 when eleven men were killed by gas. One sad tale concerned a young engaged girl who was picking ironstone nodules on a tip in Donnington Wood. Another girl asked her where the wedding reception was to be held and she replied *"In Hell"*. On that note, she lost her footing and fell down a mine shaft. Even when the mines closed they were still dangerous and there have been several cases of children falling down old shafts or unwary explorers entering disused adits and being overcome by gas. This is the real price of Britain's industrial wealth.

Field Guide

Dawley Parish Church
(SJ687064)   Here you will find the communal grave of eight miners
                            who were killed in a shaft accident at Springwell Pit in 1872.

Grange Colliery
(SJ721114)   Following the A5 east from Limekiln Bank roundabout, the site
                            of Grange Colliery is on the left. This closed in 1979 and little
                            is left other than the 1951 tandem headframe and some
                            buildings. Be careful if you visit this site as it is used by very
                            agressive nudists who react violently to the sight of cameras!
                            The Granville Colliery was the last deep mine in Shropshire
                            and this was a little further down the road where the waste
                            disposal site is now.

Grange Colliery became part of nearby Granville, which was the last coal mine in Shropshire and closed in 1979. The tandem headframe dates from 1951 and the shafts handled the upcast ventilation from Granville.

MINING IN SHROPSHIRE

Muxton Bridge Colliery
(SJ722133)

The remains of this colliery, which acted as a central pumping station for the area, are now in the Granville Country Park. They consist of the rotative beam pumping enginehouse and a very large horizontal winding enginehouse.

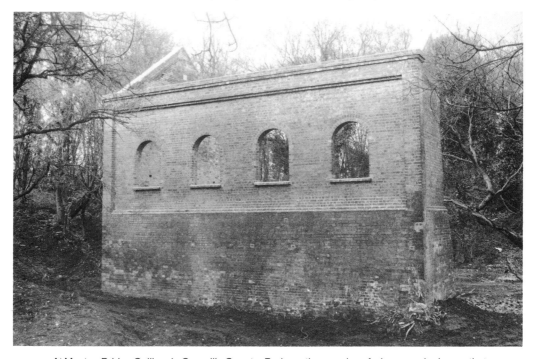

At Muxton Bridge Colliery in Granville Country Park are the remains of a large enginehouse that contained a horizontal steam winding engine. The far wall was demolished when the engine was removed to another pit.

St Michael's Church, Madeley
(SJ696041)

The site of an epitaph to John Randall, a local self-taught geologist and mining expert who wrote several books. To the rear of the church is a mosaic tombstone under a tree close to the back wall. This commemorates eight year old Arthur Turner who died at Meadow Pit in 1906 when he went to rescue his younger brother who had fallen into a ditch of boiling water (drained from the pit boilers). His mother was a mosaic worker at Maws Tile Works and made the tombstone herself. Nearby is the communal grave of nine miners who were killed in Brick Kiln Leasow Pit in 1864. The top of the vault is cast iron with a ridge for each miner but the headstone inscription is sadly becoming eroded.

**Tar Tunnel
(SJ694025)**

Situated at the foot of the Hay Inclined Plane, is the only
remaining tunnel in the Gorge which can be safely visited.
Part of the Ironbridge Gorge Museum, visitors are taken
100 yards along a brick-lined section to see a 'tar well'.
The tunnel continues further into the hillside, connecting with
coal, iron and clay mines on top of the hill, but it is not safe
to go beyond the visitor area at present.

Tuckies (SJ693024)

Boat Leasow Mine was under the Maw's Tile Works
(now a craft centre) whilst several other mines were situated
on the hillside behind the Boat Inn. Following the road past the
Boat Inn and, just before a railway bridge, the left part of the
houses on the right is the 1780s Tuckies pumping enginehouse.

MINING IN SHROPSHIRE

LILLESHALL LIMESTONE MINES
Dave Adams

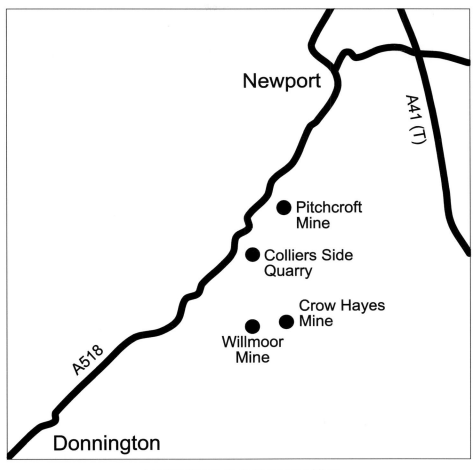

Location Map of Lilleshall Limestone Mines

MINING IN SHROPSHIRE

The volcanic mass of Lilleshall Hill, with its prominent monument to the Dukes of Sutherland, rises out of the East Shropshire Plain. It is Pre-Cambrian in origin and, with the Wrekin, amongst the oldest rocks in Europe. In later periods, the area was covered by shallow seas in which limestone was deposited and, later still, by deserts affected by earth movements and glacial erosion. The Lower Carboniferous Limestone outcrops to the east of the hill and it is split by a number of major faults. The limestone occurred in four beds and, although the shallower ones could be worked by opencast methods, deep mining was required to work the lower ones. The lower deposits made a good hydraulic cement which set under water and large quantities were used in the building of Liverpool docks.

We do not know when men first began to cut the limestone as a building material but the adjacent Lilleshall Abbey was certainly built from it in the twelfth century. Following the dissolution of the Monasteries in the 1530s, the estate was bought from the Government by the Leveson family who had made their fortune in the Wolverhampton wool trade. The family immediately set to work to exploit the land economically as it had suffered much neglect during monastic days. They drained the land, improved communications by causeways across the marshy ground on the Weald Moors and made general agricultural improvements. The family opened coal, iron and limestone mines, particularly in the area which is now north Telford. Virtually all these enterprises were contracted out to partnerships who worked the mines with varying success.

Although the earliest reference to limestone working in Lilleshall was in 1625, it was not until the eighteenth century that industry generally began to predominate. Sir John Leveson became Earl Gower in 1746 and the industrial story really began when his son Granville Leveson Gower became the second Earl in 1754. He was a typical high born gentleman of his age - landowner, Member of Parliament, Lord of the Admiralty, Lord Privy Seal and Lord Chamberlain to King George III. Despite all these duties, he took an active interest in the efficient running of the local estates, namely Sherrifhales, Lilleshall, Donnington Wood, St Georges, Priorslee, Wombridge and Snedshill.

His brother-in-law was Francis 3rd Duke of Bridgewater, who originated the first canal to be constructed in the new industrial age, which carried coal out of his Manchester mines. Through him, Earl Gower was introduced to the brothers Thomas and John Gilbert. The latter had had much experience in the cutting of the Bridgewater canal. At that time there were over 250 small pits extracting limestone in the area with varying degrees of efficiency. The Earl's agricultural improvements had led to an increased demand for lime and the expanding local iron works demanded limestone as a flux. He was thus persuaded that it would be more efficient to operate the limestone extraction directly so he and the Gilbert brothers formed the Lilleshall Partnership in 1764. The Earl also took over iron furnaces at Donnington Wood, so he now had a vested interest in producing and delivering limestone as cheaply as possible.

The new partnership soon recognised that a better communication system was required between the widely dispersed sites and in 1765 they began constructing a canal. It ran from Pave Lane to the Earl's furnaces at Donnington Wood and was known as the

Donnington Wood Canal. The quarries in Lilleshall village were improved and this included one under what is now the Sylvan Close housing estate. By the eighteenth century it was abandoned and flooded and became home to a massive pike which attacked fishermen and even pulled the Parish Clerk into the water! The pike was eventually caught in 1767 when a ditch was dug from the Boundary Brook to drain the quarry, which was then expanded into what became known as Colliers Side Quarry.

This expansion entailed the removal of a large quantity of overburden to get at the limestone. A length of canal was dug to a nearby kettle hole and the spoil taken there in tub boats to fill in marshy ground and make it suitable for agriculture. The quarry workings were linked to the main canal near Hugh's Bridge by a branch canal which was unfortunately 18 metres lower. To overcome this, the branch canal went under the main canal in a tunnel with a shaft to link the two. Boats would be moored underneath the shaft and a crane lifted pallets of stone up to other boats in the canal above.

Although some quarries could work the two shallowest limestone beds by opencast methods, to reach the lower beds they had to deep mine the limestone as it cost too much to remove the overlying strata. This also applied where shallower beds dipped downwards and the overburden increased proportionately. The mines were worked on the pillar and stall system which left a quarter of the limestone behind as pillars to support the roof. Tunnels were driven down a dip about 9 metres wide and, after about 18 metres, the tunnels were linked by a cross passage also 9 metres wide. The process would then be repeated, leaving a series of pillars about 9 metres square. For shallow beds, the mine passages would start from the existing quarry face but, for lower beds, a shaft would be sunk to the appropriate level and the same mining system employed.

Deep Kiln and Tunnel at Colliers Side Quarry, Lilleshall.

MINING IN SHROPSHIRE

Some of the limestone was converted to quicklime on site by burning it in kilns. These consisted of 7.5 metre deep shafts with a grate at the bottom connected to the outside by a horizontal service tunnel. They were fuelled by coal carried on the canal from the nearby Donnington collieries. The limestone and fuel were stacked at the shaft bottom, the fuel set alight and the whole thing left to burn for several days. A draught along the tunnel and up the chimney shaft increased the temperature. After the fire had died down, the lime was broken up into small lumps for transport. Transport of limestone and coal to the kilns themselves was originally by horse and cart but these were later replaced by lines of 'L' shaped cast iron rails. As quicklime becomes caustic when wet, it was not advisable to transport it by rail, so it was usually stored by the kilns and picked up by customers themselves.

Although some of the limestone was converted to slaked lime for cement and local land improvement schemes, the majority was sent to be used as a flux in the iron furnaces. It was transported on the canal in long lines of tub boats which were 6 metres long, 1.9 metres wide and 1.2 metres deep. It was usually transported directly from the quarry to the iron works on the intricate network of canals in the area without being transhipped.

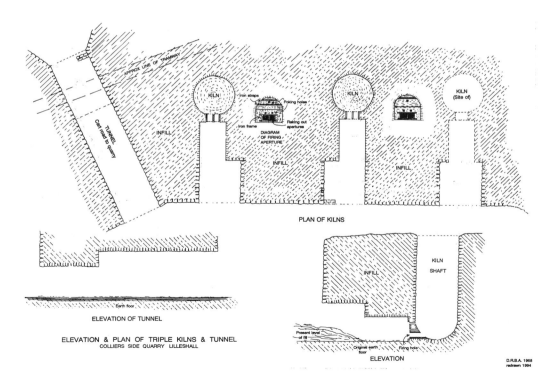

Plan and elevation of kilns at Colliers Side Quarry, Lilleshall.

The access tunnel of a limekiln at Colliers Side Quarry, Lilleshall. At the back is the hearth and, above it, several holes allowing the charge to be poked to break up the lime.

A Shropshire Canal tub boat. One horse could pull trains of up to twenty tubs, each loaded with between three and five tons of limestone or coal.

Close up of a tub boat.

The quarries at Colliers Side originally worked the shallower beds opencast but the workings were eventually continued underground with inclines linking them to the tramways above. The extracted waste material was used to build great embankments across the quarry in which kilns were built, as well as two tunnels for access. Tramways ran along the top of the embankment to feed the kilns and to carry material to the canal. Shafts from 45-75 metres deep were sunk to work the lower beds and an open trench west of Limekiln Lane was continued underground.

The Lilleshall Partnership was creating a profitable business from the Colliers Side quarries and this was not unnoticed by the neighbouring Leeke family. Their land was in the parish of Church Aston but they were landowners rather than industrialists. Their main venture was at Blackberry Bank Mine, which had originally worked in the seventeenth century, and they sunk shafts over 36 metres deep. Pumping engines, probably of the Newcomen type, were erected but they were less successful than they expected. So they leased the exploration rights to the partnership, whose canal system linked up with Blackberry Bank Mine by 1798. By this time, however, the mine was almost worked out and they had sunk several 120 metre deep shafts to the east at what was to become the Pitchcroft Mine.

*This is how the area around 'Dog Shaft' at Pitchcroft Mine may have appeared around 1858.
(Drawing by Malcolm Newton based on a reconstruction by David Adams.)*

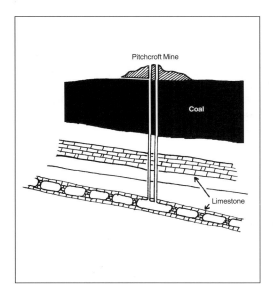

*A geological cross-section of Pitchcroft Mine
showing the coal measures near the surface,
with several limestone strata below.*

*Pitchcroft Mine was very successful until it flooded
in 1860. The SCMC member in the shaft has
stopped just above a level which originally led to
a canal basin. The water surface below conceals
another 120 metres of flooded shaft.*

MINING IN SHROPSHIRE

By 1800, the mining industry of the area was at its height but the partnership was almost finished. Both the Gilberts were dead and Earl Gower was seventy-nine. The younger son, Lord Granville Leveson-Gower, acquired all the shares in the partnership and formed the Lilleshall Company in 1802 with John Bishton, James Birch, John Onions and William Phillips. The Blackberry Bank Mine was abandoned and other quarries and mines around Lilleshall were finished by the 1830s. Although twin exploratory shafts 213 metres deep were sunk at Crow Hayes, work now concentrated on the Pitchcroft Mine.

This mine worked in a restricted area but may have produced over a million tons of limestone during its life. In 1846, the Stafford-Wellington railway was built which passed right by the main shaft of the mine. A short branch was built to the mine to facilitate limestone transport to the Donnington furnaces. The mine was notorious for accidents and a typical one occurred in 1858 in which three men were killed when *"an immense layer of stone"* fell on them.

In 1860 a real disaster struck when water was found to be rising through the floor in old workings. This rapidly became a flood and the miners had to abandon the workings when the pumps could not keep pace with the inrush. No human lives were lost but the pit ponies could not be rescued and they were left to their fate, the rotting carcases polluting local water supplies for some time afterwards. It was estimated that over 300 gallons of water per minute were entering the mine and portable pumps capable of removing 400 gallons per minute were brought in. Within days, however, the inflow had doubled and the mine was lost. It is believed that exploratory workings had passed through the Brocton Fault and found workable stone at a different level. They abandoned the workings in the fault to perhaps be mined later. Beyond the fault, however, was the North Shropshire aquifer (a large area of land which holds water like a sponge) and over a period the pressure built up until the water eventually burst into the workings. Tunnelling through this fault would have been like drilling into the bottom of a full bath. After this nothing could have saved the mine. Reserves had to be found elsewhere and attention turned to the Willmoor Mine.

Willmoor was originally called Sour Leasow Pit and had begun as twin exploratory shafts 60 metres deep, rapidly expanding to meet the local needs for limestone. The mine was finally abandoned in 1883 but produced about 188,000 tons of limestone during 21 years of working. It averaged 7,500 tons per year which was taken to a small basin on the nearby canal and carried in tub boats to the furnaces. It met its demise when the Company discovered they could bring in limestone cheaper from Wenlock Edge and Nantmawr near Oswestry, despite the extra distance involved.

Thus ended the industrial history of Lilleshall and the surrounding area. All mine buildings and equipment were removed and the dumps planted with trees. The workings flooded and the shafts were capped with brick 'beehives'. The tramways were removed and the canal system became derelict. Part of the main course was filled in during the construction of Lilleshall Hall drive in 1896.

A broken brick 'beehive' capping a shaft.

Field Guide

LIMEKILNS   There used to be numerous limekilns around the area but many have now totally vanished and the scant remains of others lie lost in the undergrowth. The best remains (SJ734164) are a bank of three served by the tramway of the Colliers Side Quarry. Leave Barrack Lane at a point opposite the old quarry stables, now a house erroneously called 'The Barracks', and follow a path leading up onto the old quarry tramway. Immediately on the left of the tramway path are two kiln shafts 7.6m deep surrounded by barbed wire (there were originally three). Now retrace your steps to turn right and down to find three tunnels set in a stone revetment, two of which are 6m long to the grates. Nearby is a 12.5m long tunnel which passed beneath the tramway which connected the kilns to the quarry face.

Continue down the path for 50m to find the remains of a much larger kiln. This is 10m long to a well preserved grate and the 10.6m shaft above is further along the tramway path above. Nearby is another tunnel, now blocked at the far end, which also led under the tramway. Take care in this area. Attempts have been made in the past to attach safety bars to the kilns. These are now lying flat and are more dangerous than the kilns themselves.

MINING IN SHROPSHIRE

CANALS   The majority of the original canal system has been filled
                           in but there are remnants in several places, some on
                           private ground:-

a) Main Line

- SJ760166   Some canal age buildings survive behind the Norwood
                           Restaurant on the Wolverhampton Road at Pave Lane.
                           The terminus is now a modern farmyard.
- SJ756163   Bridge taking Pitchcroft Lane over a short section of canal.
- SJ752160   Bridge over the drive to Lilleshall Hall National Sports Centre.
                           The drive was laid along the canal bed in 1896.
- SJ752159   Cotes Pool, a canal feeder pond.
- SJ750157/749156   Short length in water leading to the destroyed Littlehales Bridge.
- SJ740151   The Incline with basin, cottages (now modernised), boatbuilding
                           shed and entrance to pre-incline tunnel and shaft system.
- SJ739150   Stable for canal horses.
- SJ739149   Hughes Bridge and canal cottages
                           (best place to start walk to Lilleshall).
- SJ739144/736140   Length of canal to Abbey Road.
- SJ738142   Abbey Bridge (private) to rear of Lilleshall Abbey.
- SJ736140   Abbey Road Bridge.

b) Lilleshall Branch

- SJ740151/734162   Incline to Lilleshall - towpath walk.
- SJ738154   Stoplock and plug outlet.
- SJ737157   Small basin for Willmoor Mine.
- SJ736158   Remains of Willmoor Bridge.
- SJ736158   View north-east of site of Pitchcroft arm and basins now filled.

c) Pitchcroft Branch

- SJ739170   Canal cottage and short length of canal to Pitchcroft Bridge.
- SJ739170   Pitchcroft Bridge.
- SJ739171   Pitchcroft Mine basin and site of railway interchange.

MINES

**Pitchcroft Mine
(SJ739172)**   The main tip is to the south-east of the A518 and covered
                           with trees. If you have permission, take the rough path over
                           the barbed wire fence from the north-west corner and climb up,
                           passing a limekiln shaft on the right. A fenced off area on the
                           summit protects the twin drawing shafts, now protected by
                           sections of aircraft runway matting. The nearest shaft is flooded

18m down but was originally 137m deep. It has an unloading platform above the water which originally led out to the canal basin. The other shaft was 127m deep and has a protective brick beehive. To the south of the dump are the holding down bolts for the last engine.

North Shaft (SJ740173) is to the north of the A518 in a tree covered mound. It was sunk in 1857 and has now been capped. Last Shaft (SJ738173) is only distinguishable as a few humps and tree covered bumps. It is at the bottom of the Last Inn field, adjacent to the old railway line. South Shaft (SJ738169) is in an isolated tree covered mound to the south of Pitchcroft Lane. There are four limekiln tunnels buried in the undergrowth on the western side but no trace of the shaft. Except for the Last Inn field, these sites belong to Sir G T Williams Ltd, Brockton Grange.

Colliers Side Quarry (SJ735165)

One entrance is along the old tramway alignment from SJ734163, which is a public right of way, and another is in Barrack Lane opposite 'The Barracks'. From the latter, the ruined shed immediately on the left is the old weigh house. Following the track onto the tramway proper, turn left past the kiln shafts and continue until the path slopes down through the trees. This is the old incline and at the bottom is the flooded quarry. The footpath is blocked to the north by flooded ground. The more intrepid can turn left here and fight through the undergrowth to find the barred entrance to the only open underground workings left in Lilleshall. Following the pool edge southwards leads to a peninsula which divided the upper and lower open workings, now the main and round pools. Retracing your steps, the first path on the left is a second incline which joins the first and takes you back to the top of the quarry.

The Nook (SJ734165) is now a long black and white house north-east of Barrack Lane and is the last remaining eighteenth century barrack block built for quarry workers. Originally it would have been split into a number of two-room apartments. It is private but can be viewed over the hedge from the lane. It and the adjacent Sylvan Close estate stand on the site of an early quarry drained and filled in 1767 to provide a maintenance yard for Colliers Side Quarry. There was a lower barrack block on the site but this has been demolished. Further up the lane in the trees beyond the Nook is the collapsed brickwork of the quarry office. Further again on the right is 'The Barracks', which was actually the quarry stables.

'The Nook' used to be a row of barracks but is now used as houses. Barrack accommodation was once common in coal and limestone mining areas where miners lived a distance away and only went back home at weekends.

FOREST OF WYRE & CLEE HILLS COALFIELDS

Nigel Chapman, Robert Evans, David Poyner, & Steve Powell

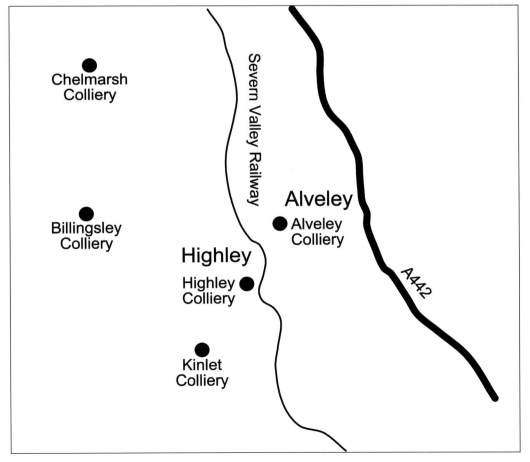

Location Map of Forest of Wyre Coalfield

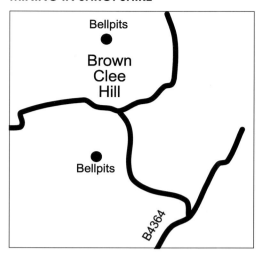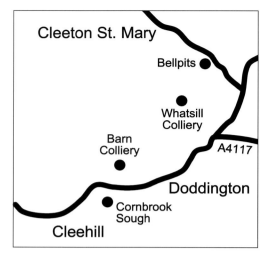

Location Map of Clee Hills Coalfield

To most people, the Wyre Forest conjures up a vision of woods and farmland so they are often surprised to learn that beneath this area lies the Wyre Forest or South Shropshire Coalfield. Some 30 kilometres long and up to 10 kilometres wide at certain points, it was mined on surface outcrops and to depths approaching 300 metres in places. The deposits start around Bridgnorth-Harpswood in the north and spread down to Abberley in the south, where faulting and changes in rock structure cut off the workable seams.

Near to the surface, there are three seams which produced a sulphurous coal - Brock Hall, Hard Mine and Main Sulphur Seams, the latter producing a fair household coal. Deeper still are four other seams - Broach, Half Yard, Four Foot and Two Foot Seams, together with ironstone and fireclay.

Mining probably started in the Middle Ages with coal dug from surface outcrops, short levels or stream beds where coal deposits were exposed. They were mostly worked by miner/farmers, who grew crops in summer and mined coal in winter when there was little farmwork to do. Most of it would have been for their personal consumption but they would have sold some locally to offset costs. By 1594, however, a proper colliery was working at Chetton on behalf of Thomas Hord of Bridgnorth and in 1613, Francis Lacon of Kinlet let his mines to John Slaney of London and Sir Percival Willoughby of Woollaton. These partners intended to develop the collieries and introduce a railway but quarrelled over the lease and parted.

The majority of collieries at this time were worked from shallow shafts, not more than 100ft deep, from which men and coal were wound by hand windlass, or occasionally a horse gin. Sometimes drift mines were worked, where tunnels were driven into the side of a hill to intersect the coal seam. None of these enterprises would have employed more than a handful of men or produced more than 100 tons of coal per year.

They were working poor quality seams and much better coal was available in neighbouring coalfields which attracted more investment.

At the start of the nineteenth century, there were dramatic, if ultimately short lived, developments at Billingsley and Highley. As demand for coal by local industry grew, a large estate at Billingsley was acquired by Sir William Pulteney, MP for Shrewsbury and a patron of Thomas Telford. He brought in the mining engineer George Johnson to develop the coal mines and, by 1796, there was a large coal works linked to a wharf on the River Severn by a 2 mile horse drawn railway. Unfortunately, the mines ran into financial difficulties and closed in 1801. A long series of court cases followed, not helped by the disappearance of Johnson's chief partner, who fled to France with all the books of the enterprise. The mines were reopened in 1803 by a consortium of local businessmen who sold them to an ironmaster George Stokes in 1810. The latter could not make the mines pay and they closed again when Stokes went bankrupt two years later.

In 1804, Stanley Colliery was opened near Highley by John and Benjamin Thompson. The brothers were ironfounders but the coal produced was too sulphurous for smelting. It found instead a market in Bewdley, Worcester and beyond for household use, hop drying, lime burning and brick making. By 1810 the colliery had three shafts sunk to 330ft and a winding engine. It was sold in 1812 but eventually closed in 1822 when the coal ran out after miners hit geological faults.

Although most workings were shallow, several deep exploratory shafts were sunk in the nineteenth century including those at Compton and Shatterford. The latter were eventually sunk to 1,380ft. Little coal was found but there was good quality clay which was mined for a brick and pottery works for several years. The small scale of working changed with the construction of the Severn Valley Railway in 1862. This provided a cheap method of transport to markets outside the area and the emphasis changed from personal consumption to external sale.

The derelict blacksmith's shop at Billingsley Colliery, with the manager's house beyond on the left.

MINING IN SHROPSHIRE

In the early 1860s, the landlord of the Cape of Good Hope Inn in Billingsley began prospecting for coal in the locality. In 1873, the shaft hit a five foot seam of coal which was to change the fortunes of the coalfield. A public company was formed in 1873 to finance the mining but faced ignominy when the chairman was sentenced to six months hard labour for fraud! It was relaunched but fared little better as the partners ended up suing each other for libel and one of the clerks was arrested at Liverpool, boarding a ship with the company's petty cash.

Buildings used by the colliery surveyors at Billingsley Colliery.

The colliery was operated on a small scale by Alfred Gibbs (the former chief clerk) until 1910, when it was purchased by the newly formed Billingsley Colliery Company. A lot of money was spent on re-equipping both underground and on the surface, where a railway was built to connect the colliery with the main line. Following the First World War, the company struggled to meet costs and there were serious geological problems, with numerous faults full of water and gas. The colliery was sold in 1915 to the Highley Mining Company who operated it until its closure during the 1921 Strike. The official statistics indicate that ironstone was mined as well but an old collier has the opinion that the only ironstone that came up the shaft was buried deep in the tubs and disguised as coal!

The Highley Mining Company was formed by several members of the Viggars family, who were engaged in the coal trade at Silverdale, Staffordshire. From the mid-1870s, they opened a brick works at Highley and began sinking trial shafts. The company was reformed in 1877 when the Viggars were joined by the Scrivener family of Newcastle-under-Lyme. In 1878, two 9ft diameter shafts were sunk and these hit the four foot thick Brooch Seam at a depth of 888ft. By 1900, about 240 men and boys were employed and this had increased to 670 by 1937. To serve the new Highley Colliery, railway sidings were created south of Highley station and a standard gauge incline was constructed up the hillside to the colliery so that main line railway trucks could be filled directly with coal from the colliery. Coal was soon being sent down the incline to the Severn Valley Railway and thence to feed the steam engines of the carpet factories in Kidderminster. Clay and shale from the waste tips were also turned into bricks for local builders.

Highley Colliery continued to run at a profit for many years and, in the early 1890s, it was decided to develop a new colliery at Kinlet. This had two shafts of 9ft and 16ft diameter, which finally reached the Brooch Seam at a depth of 927ft. A huge brick winding house was erected in 1896 with a twin cylinder horizontal steam winder inside.

The large brick enginehouse of Kinlet Colliery, built in 1896 to house a twin cylinder horizontal steamwinder.

Kinlet circa 1925.

Highley in the 1920s.

Highley. The last shift finishing on 6th November 1968

Electric locomotive at passage junction in Highley colliery in the sixties

Cramped conditions at the coal face

Aerial cableway at Highley pit   *Coal conveyor belt at Highley pit*

To serve the colliery, a short branch was taken off the Severn Valley railway in 1900, worked by a locomotive named Kinlet. Because of the steep strata, there was an underground rope haulage system which was powered by a steam engine at the shaft top. Waste material from the shaft sinking was used to create a large embankment at the pit top and a series of screens to clean the coal were built over the railway sidings. In the early 1880s, there were two mines on Chelmarsh Common and a two-storey enginehouse stood here until it was demolished in 1985. Perhaps these mines were connected with the grandiose plans at Billingsley Colliery.

By the early 1930s, Kinlet Colliery faced problems with faulting of the coal and unstable roofs. Highley Colliery, however, was very profitable and greatly mechanised with electricity underground and coal cutters. The only problem was that workings were heading under the River Severn towards Alveley and further away from the shafts. In 1935, a new shaft was started at Alveley for coal and man winding, with a concrete headgear and electric winder. It was connected to the Highley workings in 1937, at which time Kinlet Colliery was closed and the men transferred to Highley. Men and coal winding were then progressively transferred to Alveley and by 1940 Highley Colliery was closed, although the shafts at Highley were retained for ventilation. Coal was taken over the River Severn to a screening plant by a rope-worked tramway. The colliery was taken over by the NCB in 1947 and ten years later it employed 1000 men with an annual output of 300,000 tons. Geological problems and loss of markets led to the eventual closure in November 1968, with several million tons of untouched coal reserves.

Bell pits at Whatsill, Clee Hill.

To the west of the Wyre Forest Coalfield lie the Clee Hills and coal mining started here in medieval times. In 1260-3, Walter de Clifford granted a licence to Sir John de Halston to *"dig coles within the forest of La Clie to sell or give away"*. This mining was by means of adits and bellpits, the latter being shallow shafts with short passages at the bottom. As soon as there were problems with stability or ventilation, the bellpit was abandoned and another sunk next to it, spoil from the new one being tipped down the old one.

On Titterstone Clee Hill, mining continued in this way until the eighteenth century. Most of the coal was used for local lime burning. From the sixteenth century onwards, ironstone was mined as well and several furnaces were built in the surrounding area, although charcoal was used as a fuel instead of coal until the late eighteenth century. The area was a source of iron and coal in the eighteenth century for the Knight family, who were a major force in the British iron industry at that time. Iron workings were similar to the coal pits with primitive technology, relying on hand windlasses or horse gins for winding. Iron smelting continued on the hill until 1851 when the last blast furnace at Knowbury closed.

In the nineteenth century, most of the mineral rights were acquired by the ironmaster families of Lewis and Botfield and they began to develop the mines to supply coal to south-west Shropshire. By 1839, the market for the coal expanded to include north Herefordshire, Radnorshire and a great deal of Wales. Technology was introduced underground and proper collieries were developed, with steam power to allow deeper working. Drainage adits were driven to drain the workings into the Cornbrook and elsewhere. By the 1840s, there were about 250 miners producing an average of 25,000 tons of coal per year. In an attempt to ease transport of coal off the hill, a railway was built to Ludlow in the mid 1860s. This reached the top of the hill by a rope worked incline. By this time, however, the coalfield had passed its peak and the mines of Lewis and Botfield passed to a series of small private companies.

A number of mines, including Cornbrook and Whatsill Collieries, were operated by Cornbrook and Knowbury Coal & Stone Company. They had abandoned these by the end of the nineteenth century, however, as the coal began to run out. Summers and Garbett operated the Catherton Colliery until 1889 and the Whatsill Colliery was re-worked until about 1917. The Clee Hill Mining & Development Co Ltd were operating Barn Pit (the re-named Cornbrook Colliery), using Trout Pit for ventilation, until it closed in 1927. There was a brief revival during the Second World War for local use but all working had ceased by 1945.

Brown Clee Hill was the highest coalfield in England but latterly operations were on a much smaller scale than on the neighbouring hill, Titterstone Clee. By the nineteenth century, the deposits were almost exhausted and workings consisted of primitive pits mined by two or three men. Thomas Childs and Edward Duce leased the mines in 1850 and John Blunt operated a combined coal and lime works at Abdon Burf. By the end of the century, however, the industry had ceased for good.

Field Guide

WYRE FOREST COALFIELD

Alveley Colliery
(SO752842)   The large tips have been landscaped to form the Severn Valley Country Park and the colliery site is now an industrial estate. A number of buildings remain, including the lamp room, bath house, offices, workshop and weighbridge. A visitor centre in the park has a small display with photographs, plans and a mine truck. The bridge linking the colliery to the screening plant over the river survives but is scheduled for replacement. It was the first bridge in the country to be constructed by cantilever methods. At either end of the bridge are pylon bases for the aerial ropeway and, on the ground on the Highley side, the remains of an angle station and return wheel which were part of the rope-worked tramway. A footpath follows the route of the old tramway to the site of the screening plant, now a picnic site.

The return pulley wheel of the rope-worked tramway serving Alveley Colliery survives half buried, west of the Severn.

Billingsley Colliery
(SO717843)

The site is on private land but can be viewed from the road. Most of the red brick buildings date from just before the First World War and include the mine office, weigh house, power house, workshops and garage. There is a large 'bowke' for hauling coal at the edge of one of the engine beds. To the south are the remains of an incline which led to the screens. The tramway which connected the screens to the Severn Valley railway is now a footpath which leads to New England, where it crossed and re-crossed the brook

(SO727838) by means of two bridges, now collapsed, and finally a level crossing at Borle Mill (SO733827).

From a public footpath striking west opposite the Cape of Good Hope public house, it is possible to see the extensive tips of the earlier Billingsley Colliery dating from about 1800. The horse operated tramway that linked the colliery to the Severn can be traced along the east bank of the Borle Brook, running from New England (SO727838) to Brookmouth (SO753817) on a public right of way. A number of culverts and bridge abutments can just be seen.

Highley Colliery (SO747830)

The colliery offices are now houses and the bulk of the site has been turned into a country park. A winding wheel erected in 1994 as a tribute to local miners came from Bagworth Colliery, Leicestershire. The incline which linked the colliery to sidings at Highley Station is now a footpath.

Memorial to the Highley Mine

MINING IN SHROPSHIRE

Kinlet Colliery
(SO739819) All these remains are on private land. The huge enginehouse for the horizontal steam winder has the original plaque dated 1896 in the gable end. Adjacent are the remains of the associated boiler house and coal bunkers. The main winding shaft has been capped over but the headframe footings are still visible. Fifty metres to the west is the upcast shaft, with welded steel shutters covering an open shaft lined by brick with concrete reinforcing. Next to this are the remains of a Sirocco type ventilating fanhouse and a winder for the shaft.
In the undergrowth are other foundations which were probably workshops.

BROWN CLEE COALFIELD

Brown Clee Hill
(SO595865-
SO595845) The site of rounded humps of old bellpits dating back to the thirteenth century.

TITTERSTONE CLEE COALFIELD

Barn Colliery
(SO605761) The shaft has been capped but the spoil tips can still be seen. Old rails have been used as fence posts around here.

Catherton Common
(SO620780) This is an area of very old workings with remains of mounds and collapsed bellpits, on either side of the road to Cleeton St Mary.

Cornbrook Sough
(SO603756) This was a drainage level from Cornbrook Colliery but it also drained several other smaller pits on the way. It is gated and used as a water supply so there is no public access.
In the late 1960s it was explored for at least 1000ft.

Magpie Hill
(SO615775) Here are the spoil tips of Catherton and Whatsill Collieries, as well as the remains of a self-acting incline leading north-east to the Cleeton St Mary road.

SOUTH WEST SHROPSHIRE OREFIELD

Terry Davies & Adrian Pearce

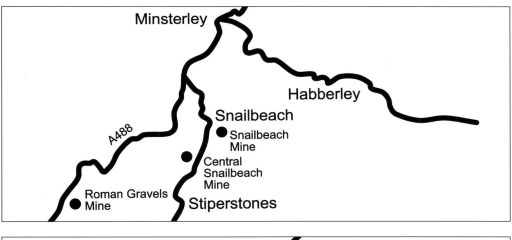

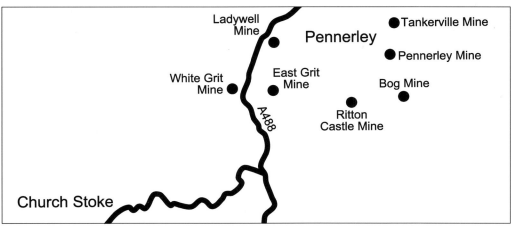

Location Map of South West Shropshire Orefield

MINING IN SHROPSHIRE

Within a four mile radius of the village of Shelve, lies an area consisting of moorland, woods and rocky outcrops, dotted with scattered farms and villages. Visitors who have the time to look can also find other features - spoil tips, tall chimneys and the roofless grey walls of old enginehouses.

Lordshill chimney

Mining remains, Snailbeach

It is hard to believe that this pleasant rural scenery was once the site of a thriving mining industry which extracted lead, zinc, copper, barytes and other minerals. In 1875, this small area produced over 10% of the UK lead ore and up to the First World War produced about 25% of UK barytes.

The Romans were possibly the first to exploit lead in this area by means of open trenches and shallow levels and shafts. Mining methods changed very little in the centuries after the Romans left and workings continued to be relatively shallow, drained by levels driven from the valley sides. Lead was a valuable commodity, however, and in 1181 Hugh Pentalf (Sheriff of Shropshire) accepted £55 from the King's lead mines at Shelve. In 1182 a church in Gloucester paid 10 guineas for 34 loads of lead for the roof and in 1278 three waggonloads of lead were sent from Shelve to Builth Castle.

Roman pig of lead found at Linley near the Stiperstones,
stamped with the name of the Emperor Hadrian (AD 117-138).

As ore became exhausted, however, the miners had to go deeper and faced the problem of removing water from the workings. Where drainage levels from adjacent valleys could not solve this problem, the water was removed manually in barrels drawn up the shaft by windlass or horse whim. Other mines used waterwheels to operate pumps but they relied on the water supply which tended to dry up in summer and freeze in winter, causing the lower workings to flood. This state of affairs continued until the late eighteenth century when the invention of the steam engine revolutionised the local mining industry. In 1775, Boulton and Watt formed their famous partnership and began to manufacture steam engines near Birmingham. The mine adventurers of Shropshire were not slow to take advantage of this new means of power and nine Boulton and Watt engines are recorded at local mines before 1800. Boulton and Watt began to lose their monopoly after 1800 and engines from other manufacturers appeared on the scene. The mining industry started to expand and by 1850 the view from the Stiperstones would have included a dozen enginehouses, each with its tall chimney capped with a plume of smoke. By the 1870s, there were seventeen engines at work in the Rea Valley alone, with four more on order.

Steam engines worked by introducing steam into a vertical cylinder fitted with a moving piston, thus forcing the piston down the cylinder. This piston was connected to the end of a beam which was pivoted on the wall of the enginehouse, with the other end projecting over the shaft. As the piston was pushed down the cylinder, it pulled down the 'indoor' end of the beam and thus raised the 'outdoor' end. In most engines, the outdoor end of the beam was attached to a series of joined pump rods in the shaft which were connected to pumps at the shaft bottom. As the piston came to the end of its stroke, the weight of the pump rods pulled the outdoor end of the beam back down and thus raised the piston back to the top of the cylinder. In other engines, the beam was attached to a crank which operated a winding drum or crushing machinery.

Pumping engine

Winding engine

Boulton & Watt did not manufacture everything on their engines, only the more specialised parts. John Wilkinson's foundry at Bersham made the cylinders and the rest was made by local blacksmiths and mechanics on site, using plans and drawings supplied by the partners. Payment for the engine was also unusual in that it was not an outright sale. An annual payment was negotiated, based on fuel costs shown by the engine as compared with a Newcomen engine of the same power. These payments were to last until the partners' patent expired in 1800. In South Shropshire, where some of the mines found it hard just to keep in business, the partners must have found it difficult to collect their dues.

The erection of a new pumping engine at a mine was quite an important event and at the Bog Mine in 1838 *"Mr Cross of Chester put in motion a steam engine of 370 horsepower to conquer the deluge of water. About 1pm, this grand piece of machinery began to have fresh fuel added to its boilers and for several moments the spectators were breathless with anxiety till the beam lifted its majestic head and Mr Cross named her "The Queen Victoria" amidst the tremendous cheering of a vast multitude, the band playing "God Save the Queen". The company retired to a large booth where several hogsheads of most excellent ale and large quantities of bread and cheese were distributed to the workmen and multitude after which some hundreds footed it on the "light fantastic toe" to Cambria's favourite instrument, the harp and two violins, while members sat down to an excellent dinner in the office of the company and adjoining rooms".*

Production of lead reached a peak in the latter half of the nineteenth century but, by 1885, cheap imports from abroad had caused the price to drop from a high of £20 to only £11 per ton. This brought disaster to many of the district's smaller mines which could not make a profit at this price and had to close. Even the larger mines were on the wane by 1900 and they had to turn to mining barytes to make ends meet. Huglith Mine was the last large mine but this closed in 1947 and there has been no serious mining since.

This attractive enginehouse at Snailbeach Mine was built in 1881 to house steam-powered compressors for the pneumatic drills used underground.

The compressor house before restoration.

Although miners were brought in from places such as Cornwall or Derbyshire, most of the men who worked here were locals. Their women and children worked on the surface crushing and preparing the ore for smelting (a process known as dressing the ore). They had to work in all kinds of weather with minimum shelter, a miserable life that would never be condoned today. Adjacent to many of the mines you will find ruins of houses which were abandoned when the mines closed forever. If you walk to the head of Perkinsbeach Dingle or Blakemoorgate you can see the remains of whole abandoned villages.

Some miners lived in villages, but many more preferred to live in smallholdings scattered over the surrounding hillsides. Landowners encouraged their miners to squat on their land and to make small enclosures. In this way, they could collect rent from the miner as well as obtaining his labour. From his cottage, the miner used to walk many miles to the mine, both day and night in all kinds of weather. There was no social security in those days and the miner had a stark choice, if he did not work he did not get paid. To offset this, many miners formed friendly societies which would pay out a weekly sum if members were off work due to sickness or accident. Each cottage had a number of acres of land and this allowed the families to supplement their income by growing most of their own food. An irate mine owner of the nineteenth century was led to remark that, because they cultivated their own land, the miners were not entirely dependent upon their earnings at the mine for subsistence. This was apparently an undesirable trend as it made the miners too independent! Their houses were small with no more than two bedrooms upstairs and a living room and pantry downstairs, occasionally with lean-to buildings at the side. The miners built their own houses out of local stone with a thatched roof. Their neighbours often lent a hand. Outbuildings were also thatched but the walls were made with a frame of wood filled with a mixture of gorse, turves and mud.

A typical squatters cottage being rebuilt at Ironbridge Museum. A miner and his family could have lived in a cottage such as this, with a few acres of land for crops, pigs and chickens.

The smallholding was usually sufficient to provide enough grazing for the milking cow in summer and hay to last the winter, while some miners also kept pigs for bacon or as porkers. Poultry were common, as were sheep which were allowed to roam the hillsides. Since the miner's family tended to be large, he had no choice but to be a keen gardener, using his vegetable plot as an important additional food supply. The children were expected to help out by collecting whinberries and blackberries from as far away as the Long Mynd to supplement the family diet. This was so important that schoolmasters often had to close the local school at those times of the year when wayside fruits were ripe. A miner's main meal might consist of bacon and vegetable stew with homemade bread. To eat meat supplied by the butcher was highly unusual.

Because of their proximity to the mines, these smallholdings were sometimes threatened by subsidence when workings approached too close to the surface. In 1897 a Mr Jones complained to the Snailbeach Mine. A survey showed that the workings had approached to within 20 yards of his house and that they were 12ft wide at a depth of 14ft. The company offered to buy Jones' house to work the vein as an open cutting. Jones swiftly reached a decision to leave his home and sell out to the company.

In the larger mines men worked eight hour shifts for five days a week. On Saturdays only a third of the miners were at work, between the hours of 6am and 12 noon. The remaining two thirds of the men were thus idle from Friday night to Monday morning. These long weekends were not usual at the time and were unpopular with the mine owners who still had to keep the mines pumped dry. All attempts to introduce a full day's work on Saturday were unsuccessful. At Roman Gravels Mine in 1870 the workers from other mines induced the men to stop Saturday working by threats and intimidation, saying that they were breaking the rules of the country. In 1871 the miners were also taking a day's holiday immediately following the monthly payday. The lunch hour, taken during the shift, was a full hour or more. All these breaks appeared to cause the mine management a great deal of frustration.

Abandoned lead miner's squatter cottages at Blakemoorgate.

MINING IN SHROPSHIRE

(Left) Mr Davies and Mr Edwards
clearing fallen rock at Huglith Mine.

(Below) One of the two blacksmiths shops
at Snailbeach Mine, with a load of drill rods
waiting to be sharpened. The miners had to pay
for the upkeep of their own tools.

Unlike modern mines, very few miners were actually full-time employees of the mining company. The exceptions were the mine captains, engineer, engine drivers and perhaps a few other specialists such as the men who maintained the shaft. It was even known for particularly skilled captains and engineers to be employed by more than one mine, dividing their time between them. All other workers were employed on a monthly contract and they had to compete to sell their skills in a type of auction known as the monthly reckoning. In this, the captain would offer different types of work for the forthcoming month and it would be given to the miners who quoted the cheapest rate. The men formed themselves into small teams and would offer to work a particular part of the mine for which the mining company would pay them an agreed rate for a set weight of ore brought to surface. Pumping and winding costs were borne by the company but the men were obliged to buy gunpowder and candles from the company. Depending on the custom, some mines accepted ore as it was brought from the mines, others required the mining teams to deliver it already dressed for smelting. In the latter case, the teams would have to employ their own people, often their families, to dress the ore on the surface. To prevent ore becoming mixed up, each kibble or wagon of ore was marked to show where it came from and was dumped at the surface in separate compartments known as ore bins.

Mine tubs underground at Snailbeach Mine.

Underground, it was up to the teams to decide how they mined the ore.
There were some restrictions, however, and the mine captain was responsible for ensuring the safety of the mine, having the right to insist that timber supports were installed if necessary. This was not particularly for the benefit of the men -
he was more concerned that the workings did not collapse and interfere with the profits!
A typical mining team consisted of two experienced miners, a labourer for the heavy shovelling and perhaps a young boy to carry the ore to the shaft bottom. The mine workings would be divided into many different working areas, each with their own mining team. It was always a gamble because, depending on the richness of the vein, a team could either make a big profit during the month or a loss. Surprisingly enough, this system was very popular with the miners who valued their independence and appreciated the chance it gave them to make good profits. It also suited the mining companies because it encouraged the teams to deliver as much ore as possible to surface.

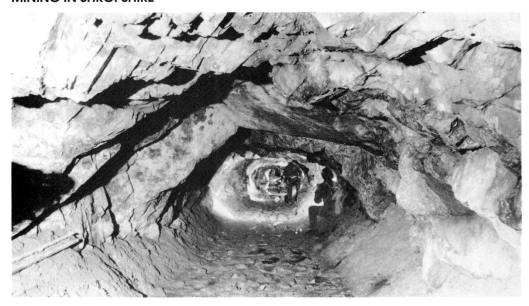

Perkins Level at Snailbeach Mine was driven during this century using compressed air drills and high explosive. This gives an uneven finish to the sides and roof but the passages are usually bigger.

The rate for a particular area of the mine could vary from month to month. If a team found a rich vein which was easily worked, they would obviously make a large profit. The mining company would then offer a lower rate for that area at the next reckoning. The ploy worked because there were always other teams willing to take on rich areas. Conversely, if an area proved poor during the month then teams would be unwilling to bid for it and the company would have to increase the rate before it was taken on. The monthly reckoning was a general holiday and schools were closed for the day. The reckoning at Roman Gravels Mine was accompanied by a fair held at the crossroads, where hard earned money could be exchanged for necessities.

The narrow gauge Snailbeach District Railway linked Snailbeach Mine to the main line railway. This is one of the six locomotives operating in the 1920s.

Local political feeling ran strongly at times and elections could engender violence between bands of rival villagers. The Hope Valley was a Tory stronghold whilst Snailbeach was staunchly for the Liberals. The supporters of each party would attempt to prove their superiority by punching the heads of their supposed inferiors.

Compared to some areas, the district was very well served by schools. Although most were small, they were very numerous and each small village had its own. The free school at Snailbeach, founded in 1843, was a typical example of one of the larger ones. It was erected at the joint expense of the Marquis of Bath and several gentlemen of the Snailbeach Company, with accommodation for one hundred pupils. Average attendance was about eighty. The company provided an endowment of £40 per annum towards the running costs and each miner was expected to pay 6d per quarter to the schoolmaster. As the mine at this time employed 500 men collecting an average total of £2,000 per month, it would seem that education was quite cheap. The schoolmaster's wage would have been £100 per annum (twice the average miner's wage) unless he chose to pay an assistant.

The mining communities were very religious and there was a strong chapel following in the district. It is significant that, of the seven men killed in the Snailbeach disaster, three were lay preachers and the other four were steady attenders. Five were Methodists and the remaining two belonged to the Church of England. The Wellington Journal of the times records that Mr Henry Wiggin of London, known as the 'Weeping Preacher', visited Snailbeach and had large audiences for night after night.

(Right) The headframe of George's Shaft at Snailbeach Mine, scene of the disaster in 1895.

(Below) The headframe of George's Shaft collapsed in 1974. It may be restored at a future date.

MINING IN SHROPSHIRE

Sunday Schools thrived and the big occasions of the year were the treats. In hard times, these might only consist of marching behind a local brass band, followed by a picnic on top of Corndon Hill. Later trips were made with the children riding in horse drawn wagons and eventually in charabancs to places as far away as Rhyl. The chapels organised Eisteddfodau at holiday times with singing competitions. Another popular local activity was football. Thrift was encouraged by the Chapel clothing clubs and charity took such forms as paying a child's school pence when the father died.

Accidents were common in the local mines and one of the worst was the Snailbeach Mine disaster which cost seven lives on 6th March 1895. The winding system at George's Shaft consisted of two separate cages (later converted to a single cage), each of which had its own rope passing over pulleys on the headgear to the same drum. The ropes wound on the drum would bring one cage to surface at the same time as the other cage was at the shaft bottom. On the morning of the accident George Williams, the engineman, ran the cages three times through the shaft as a test. He then raised two cage loads of night shift men before lowering the morning shift. When the third cage load of seven men were half way down the shaft the rope broke.

One of the miners at the shaft bottom was W Holyoake, who said *"When we got down we lighted our candles and waited till the next party should come down. In two or three minutes we heard the cage coming down. The noise was like thunder. The cage crashed down with the bodies in it. The cage was smashed up. The rope came down on top of the cage. We signalled up at once and proceeded to take the rope away by drawing it along the level. The rope was knocked about. We had to knock the cage to pieces to get the bodies out. There was no sign of life in any of them. I had every confidence in the rope and it always looked perfectly safe."*

This spiral classifier and jigs at Snailbeach Mine were used for separating the ore by gravity.
They have been removed for future restoration.

The top part of the winding rope recoiled out of the shaft and George Williams the engineman had a narrow escape. Members of the day shift waiting at the shaft bottom were treated to the sight of the 7ft 6ins high cage reduced to a mere 18ins by the smash and yet, when the rescue party descended the ladders to recover the mutilated bodies, a watch worn by one of the dead was still ticking. After adjustments to the winding engine, the bodies were brought to surface in the second cage. The verdict at the inquest was *"accidental death caused by the breakage of a defective rope"*.
The jury thought that the rope had been neglected and had been in use for too long. Although the Mines Inspector thought that the company and their agents should be censured, there was no breach of the Metalliferous Mines Regulation Act as it stood at that time.

Rope breakage was not the only danger faced at the mine. In 1897, a particularly lucky miner named William Lewis slipped off a ladder whilst climbing up the shaft at the 282 yard level. He fell to the bottom, suffering nothing more serious than a few bruises. An investigation revealed that the ladders were in good working order and concluded that Lewis had been careless. As in many hard rock mining areas, Shropshire miners also had to face the problem of silicosis when rock drills were introduced. It was not until later in the twentieth century that regulations were introduced to reduce the amount of dust produced by these machines. Most drills used water to damp down the dust emission but Huglith, Gatten and Sallies Mines used suction containers to collect the dust and the miners wore masks. For many miners, however, the regulations came too late and they were condemned to die early from pneumonia and other dust-related diseases.

A processing shed for barytes at Snailbeach Mine. Now unfortunately collapsed but may be restored in future.

Overhead mining for barytes in Sallies Mine in 1946. The risk of silicosis from rock dust had recently been realised. The miners are wearing face masks and using a suction device to remove dust from the air.

Field Guide

Bog Mine (SO358978)   A lead mine worked during the eighteenth to twentieth centuries. The site is owned by the County Council who have erected some interpretation boards near the car park. The magazine is intact and next to it is the grilled Somme Tunnel.

The magazine at Bog Mine where gunpowder and fuses were stored.

(Above) Traction engine used by Bog Mine to transport lead ore to the smelter at Minsterley.

(Right) Tower of aerial cableway that replaced road haulage of lead ore from Bog Mine to the smelter.

MINING IN SHROPSHIRE

Central Snailbeach Mine (SJ368016)

A lead mine worked during the nineteenth century. The winding enginehouse has been converted into a private dwelling and the stub of the square chimney can be seen from the road.

Truncated chimney and enginehouse of New Central Mine, now converted to a dwelling.

East Grit Mine (SO327980)

A large lead mine reputedly worked from Roman times up to the twentieth century. The winding enginehouse for New Engine Shaft is fairly intact but that for Old Grit Engine Shaft to the east only consists of one wall.

Ruins of the enginehouse by New Engine Shaft at East Grit Mine.

**Ladywell Mine
(SO328992)**

A lead mine worked during the nineteenth century.
The enginehouse for the steam winder stands beside
the road and is almost intact.

The attractive brick and stone enginehouse of Ladywell Mine.

**Pennerley Mine
(SO352988)**

A lead mine worked during the eighteenth to twentieth centuries.
There are remains of enginehouses and other buildings
on either side of the road.

**Ritton Castle Mine
(SO341977)**

A lead mine worked during the nineteenth century.
The enginehouse and chimney are still fairly intact and in the
valley below are the remains of a waterwheel pit.

The ruins of the enginehouse and chimney at Ritton Castle Mine.

MINING IN SHROPSHIRE

Roman Gravels Mine
(SO333999)

A lead mine reputedly worked from Roman times up to the twentieth century. Large tips can be seen beside the road but most other features have been destroyed. On the hillside are several hushes, or eroded valleys, where lead is exposed, reputed to be of Roman origin.

Snailbeach Mine
(SJ375022)

A lead and barytes mine reputedly worked from Roman times up to 1955. This was the biggest lead mine in Shropshire and it is said to have yielded the greatest volume of lead per acre of any mine in Europe. The surface buildings rank amongst the best in the country. Shropshire County Council own most of the buildings and are preserving them at the time of writing.
It is hoped that an interpretation trail may be set up in the future. Leave your car in the car park at the bottom of the mine tips and walk up the hill to the mine. Of the many features, the most impressive are Black Tom shaft & engine shed, blacksmiths shop, candlehouse, compressor house & chimney, crusher house, Day Level, George's Shaft & engine houses, offices, locomotive shed, Lordshill Shaft & engine houses, Lordshill chimney, magazine, orehouse, Perkins Level, Chapel Shaft & engine house.

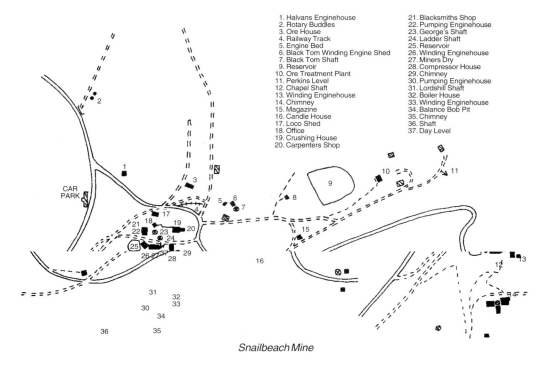

1. Halvans Enginehouse
2. Rotary Buddles
3. Ore House
4. Railway Track
5. Engine Bed
6. Black Tom Winding Engine Shed
7. Black Tom Shaft
9. Reservoir
10. Ore Treatment Plant
11. Perkins Level
12. Chapel Shaft
13. Winding Enginehouse
14. Chimney
15. Magazine
16. Candle House
17. Loco Shed
18. Office
19. Crushing House
20. Carpenters Shop
21. Blacksmiths Shop
22. Pumping Enginehouse
23. George's Shaft
24. Ladder Shaft
25. Reservoir
26. Winding Enginehouse
27. Miners Dry
28. Compressor House
29. Chimney
30. Pumping Enginehouse
31. Lordshill Shaft
32. Boiler House
33. Winding Enginehouse
34. Balance Bob Pit
35. Chimney
36. Shaft
37. Day Level

Snailbeach Mine

Lordshill enginehouse at Snailbeach Mine.

**Tankerville Mine
(SO355995)**

A lead mine worked during the nineteenth and twentieth centuries. The remains of the enginehouse and square chimney can be seen from the road.

The enginehouse and chimney at Watsons Shaft, Tankerville Mine.

Tankerville Mine about 1871. The headframe on the left is over Watsons Shaft.

White Grit Mine
(SO319980)

A lead mine reputedly worked from Roman times up to the twentieth century. The enginehouse is fairly complete by the side of the road and the magazine is opposite.

Ruined enginehouse of White Grit Mine.

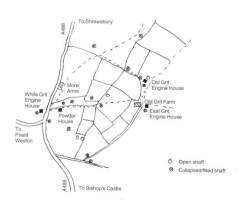

Site guide to the Grit Mine.

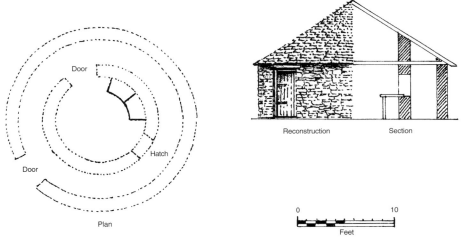

Door

Door

Hatch

Plan

Reconstruction

Section

0   10

Feet

Reconstructed magazine, or explosive store, of White Grit Mine.

Wotherton Mine
(SJ277005)

The old pumping and winding enginehouse is in good condition and can be seen from the road. A dwelling was built onto the side after the mine was abandoned.

Barytes miners in Wotherton, Chirbury circa 1900.
The miners candles are stuck to their helmets with lumps of clay.

Enginehouse of Wotherton Mine.

GLOSSARY

ADIT	Horizontal tunnel into a mine.
ADVENTURERS	Shareholders in a mine.
BARGAIN	Agreement between mine captain and mining team to mine ore for a set price for a month.
BARRACKS	Building at a mine where miners lodged during the week.
BEEHIVE	A brick or stone dome built over the top of an abandoned shaft.
BOB	The beam of a steam engine or balance box.
BORER	Drill rod.
BUCKING IRON	Flat faced tool for crushing lead ore.
BUDDLE	Structure over which a flow of water passes to separate lead ore from waste.
CAPTAIN	Experienced mine manager.
CLACK	A pump valve.
COPE	To agree to mine ore for a fixed sum.
COUNTRY ROCK	The strata through which the vein passes.
CROSS CUT	A level driven in barren rock for access.
DAMP	Gas.
DEADS	Waste rock, often stacked underground.
DIAL	Miner's surveying compass.
DRIFT	See ADIT.
FATHOM	Unit of measurement - 6 feet.
FLATRODS	Horizontal beams for transmitting motion from an engine or waterwheel to a shaft some distance away.
FOOTRID	See ADIT.

MINING IN SHROPSHIRE

GAD	Wedge for splitting rock.
GIN	Engine.
GRASS	Surface of a mine.
HADE	Inclination of the lode.
HANGING WALL	Wall or side overhanging the lode.
HUSH	Narrow valley eroded by damming water and releasing it to carry away topsoil, thus exposing lead veins.
JAGGER	Packhorse driver.
JIGGER	Mechanical sieve for separating ore.
KIBBLE	Egg-shaped iron bucket for raising ore.
LANDER	Person who unloads kibble or cage at shaft top.
LAUNDER	Wooden trough for directing flow of water.
LEAT	Surface water course.
LEVEL	See ADIT.
LODE	Ore deposit.
OFFAL	Waste rock including irrecoverable ore.
OLD MAN	Miners' term for previous miner or ancient mine workings.
ORE	Mineral that was mined.
PITMAN	Miner responsible for maintenance of pitwork.
PITWORK	Pump pipes, pumps, etc in a shaft.
RIDER	Rock dividing a lode.
RISE	Underground shaft driven upwards.
SETT	Leased area of a mine.
SHAFT	Vertical entrance to a mine.
SOLE	Lowest part of a mine.
STOPE	Worked out lode, left as an open cavity.
STULL	Timber support, sometimes used to make a platform on which deads are placed.
SUMP	Underground shaft driven downwards.
TAILINGS	Waste material from ore washing process.
TAMPING IRON	Tool for packing down a charge of gunpowder.
TUBBING	Iron or timber rings in a shaft to support brickwork.
TUTWORK	Method of work similar to piece work.

WHIM	Winding engine, either horse or steam powered.
WINDER	Steam engine used for winding in a shaft.
WINDLASS	Hand operated winch for pulling loads up a shaft.
WINZE	Underground shaft.

Wooden windlass over shaft.

MINING IN SHROPSHIRE

FURTHER READING

"A Survey of the Metal Mines of South Shropshire",
  S Holding, 1993, Account 12 Shropshire Caving & Mining Club.

"Coal Mining in the Clee Hills of South Shropshire",
  G Price, 1968, Transactions Birmingham Enterprise Club 2.

"Industries of the Morda Valley",
  R D Thomas, 1939, Shropshire Libraries.

"Metalliferous Mines of Shropshire Vol.1 - Gazetteer",
  A Pearce, 1994, Account 20 Shropshire Caving & Mining Club.

"Mines & Mineral Workings in the Coalbrookdale Coalfield",
  I Brown, 1979, Account 11 Shropshire Caving & Mining Club.

"Mining Remains in South West Shropshire",
  T Davies, M Newton & A Pearce, 1994, Account 18 Shropshire Caving & Mining Club.

"Rural Colliers of Wyre",
  S Davies, 1983/84, Folk Life 22.

"Survey of the Church Aston - Lilleshall Mining Area",
  D Adams, 1970, Account 7 Shropshire Caving & Mining Club.

"The Coming of Coal; Industrial Development in a South Shropshire Parish",
  G Nair & D Poyner, 1993, Midland History 18.

"The Mines of Lilleshall & Church Aston, Shropshire",
  D Coxill, 1992, Account 16 Shropshire Caving & Mining Club.

MINING IN SHROPSHIRE

"The Mines of Llanymynech Hill",
  D Adams & A Pearce, 1992, Account 14 Shropshire Caving & Mining Club.

"The Mines of Shropshire",
  I Brown, 1976, Moorland Publishing Company.

"The Shropshire Lead Mines",
  F Brook & M Allbutt, 1973, Moorland Publishing Company.

"The Wyre Forest Coalfield",
  R Evans, 1979, Bewdley Museum Information Sheet.

"The Wyre Forest Coalfield",
  R Evans & D Poyner, 1994, Cleobury Chronicles 3.

"Titterstone Clee Hills ; Everyday Life, Industrial History & Dialect",
  A Jenkins, 1982, privately published.

More books on Shropshire's industrial past
published by Shropshire Books

CANALS OF SHROPSHIRE	Richard K Morriss	£ 4.99
RAILWAYS OF SHROPSHIRE	Richard K Morriss	£ 5.99
SHROPSHIRE RAILWAYS PICTORIAL		£ 5.50
HISTORIC BRIDGES OF SHROPSHIRE	Anthony Blackwall	£ 5.50
SHROPSHIRE FROM THE AIR	Michael Watson & Chris Musson	£13.99

for a complete list of Shropshire Books titles,
please contact:

Shropshire Books,
Information & Community Services Department,
Winston Churchill Building,
Radbrook Centre,
SHREWSBURY SY3 9BJ.
Telephone: 01743 254043.